HIGH-TEMPERATURE
CHEMISTRY

CURRENT AND FUTURE PROBLEMS

A Conference Organized at Rice University, Houston, Texas
January 26–27, 1966
by the
COMMITTEE ON HIGH-TEMPERATURE CHEMICAL PHENOMENA
of the
DIVISION OF CHEMISTRY AND CHEMICAL TECHNOLOGY
NATIONAL ACADEMY OF SCIENCES
NATIONAL RESEARCH COUNCIL
with support of the
AIR FORCE OFFICE OF SCIENTIFIC RESEARCH

Publication 1470
NATIONAL ACADEMY OF SCIENCES
NATIONAL RESEARCH COUNCIL
Washington, D. C.   1967

Conference supported by the Directorate of Chemical Sciences, Air Force Office of Scientific Research, under Grant No. AF-AFOSR-1040-66.

Available from
Printing and Publishing Office
National Academy of Sciences
2101 Constitution Avenue
Washington, D.C. 20418

Library of Congress Catalog Card Number: 67-60010

Preface

Since its inception in 1961, the National Research Council Committee
on High-Temperature Chemical Phenomena has had as its goal the promotion and coordination of activities concerned with high-temperature
phenomena and related aspects of materials science. The high-temperature field is an active interdisciplinary area involving chemistry, physics, metallurgy, ceramics, and various engineering fields. The techniques—to "room-temperature" men, at least—are designed for extremes, and high-temperature phenomena are often quite different
from those predicted from low-temperature analogies. New kinds of
apparatus along with unexpected reactions, new molecules, and other
scientific surprises are commonplace in high-temperature research;
thus, the high-temperature scientist often has to adapt or innovate.

In recognition of the current importance of high-temperature phenomena and the clearly established needs for a much more complete
understanding, the Committee organized a Conference on Current and
Future Problems in High-Temperature Chemistry, which was held at
Rice University on January 26-27, 1966. There were 48 participants,
21 of whom presented papers; 20 of these papers are printed here,
either in full or as abstracts. In addition, questions and answers from
the floor are given at the end of several papers, and conclusions based
on a questionnaire circulated to the participants are summarized. Several postmeeting contributions are also included.

The meeting was sponsored by the National Academy of Sciences -
National Research Council, with financial support through a grant from
the United States Air Force Office of Scientific Research; facilities
were kindly provided by Rice University. Travel arrangements for a
number of the participants were provided by their own laboratories.

It is the hope of the Committee on High-Temperature Chemical Phenomena that this volume can serve as a window into the future, revealing unsolved problems and highlighting the many unexplored potentialities of chemical research at high temperatures to those who wonder what scientists in this field are doing now or what they wish to do in the future.

October 31, 1966   John L. Margrave, Chairman
Committee on High-Temperature
Chemical Phenomena

Division of Chemistry and Chemical Technology

PAUL J. FLORY, Stanford University, Chairman
MARTIN A. PAUL, Executive Secretary

COMMITTEE ON HIGH-TEMPERATURE CHEMICAL PHENOMENA

JOHN L. MARGRAVE, Rice University, Chairman

MELVIN G. BOWMAN, Los Alamos Scientific Laboratory

WILLIAM A. CHUPKA, Argonne National Laboratory

DANIEL CUBICCIOTTI, Stanford Research Institute

PAUL W. GILLES, University of Kansas

DONALD L. HILDENBRAND, Douglas Advanced Research Laboratory

S. S. PENNER, University of California, San Diego

THOMAS B. REED, Massachusetts Institute of Technology

HAROLD L. SCHICK, Lockheed Missiles and Space Company

ALAN W. SEARCY, University of California, Berkeley

WILLIAM WELTNER, JR., Union Carbide Research Institute

Contents

High Temperatures—An Extreme Condition?

JOHN L. MARGRAVE
Department of Chemistry
Rice University
Houston, Texas

On the basis of personal comfort and convenience, men have established a reference range of temperatures, which the scientist generalizes as "room temperature," meaning $\sim 298\,^{\circ}$K. Thus, $1{,}000\,^{\circ}$K, $5{,}000\,^{\circ}$K, and $20{,}000\,^{\circ}$K become "high temperature," and $50\,^{\circ}$K or less becomes "low temperature." These conditions seem to represent extremes which one is tempted to feel are either unlikely, unimportant, or only of academic interest. Actually, of course, this conclusion is far from true: the major portion of our universe is at one or the other of these extremes. Furthermore, so many industrial operations—combustion processes, electric discharges, and uses of nuclear reactors, for example—as well as stellar processes, involve high-temperature phenomena that one can regard "high temperature" as describing a common condition of matter and, therefore, a condition deserving to be well understood.

Unfortunately, the data gathered by chemists, physicists, and engineers before the 1940's were heavily concentrated in the easily accessible range of temperatures around $298\,^{\circ}$K, and only in the last 15 years has there been an extensive effort to acquire a real understanding of the high-temperature realm of $1{,}000$-$5{,}000\,^{\circ}$K. Even this effort has been clearly limited by the experimental restrictions imposed by the melting points and vapor pressures of available materials and by the lack of equipment and techniques for identification of species and for studies of reaction rates involving transient high-temperature molecules. Little quantitative work has been done at temperatures above $3{,}000\,^{\circ}$K. It is commonly held that the limit of chemistry is reached at about $15{,}000\,^{\circ}$K, yet this corresponds to an energy of only a little over 1 eV—not even enough to break a weak chemical bond.

1

It would seem to be a worthwhile goal of this conference to delineate the current status and future possibilities of high-temperature chemistry for consideration by the scientific, the engineering, the military, and the political worlds. In this vein, consider the following:

1. Our current knowledge of chemical and physical phenomena still has serious gaps in the energy range 0.1-10 eV (1,000-100,000 °K) where atoms, ions, and molecules can exist and interact.

2. In spite of the monumental achievements in synthesis by organic chemists working with only a few elements, at temperatures not far from 298 °K, it seems safe to predict that high-temperature syntheses utilizing all the elements in their various oxidation states can produce an even larger number of compounds; condensed phases can now be maintained at extremely high temperatures by use of high-pressure techniques, and reactive but transient high-temperature species can be trapped in low-temperature matrices, where their reactions may be quantitatively controlled.

3. The development of definitive fundamental theories of chemical bonding and of intramolecular and intermolecular forces will be delayed until there is an extended collection of measured thermodynamic properties, molecular parameters, and transport properties for the varied species attainable only in high-temperature environments.

Clearly, the high-temperature frontier offers one of the most exciting challenges to modern scientists. It is to be hoped that this collection of papers will illustrate most vividly the importance, the potentialities, and the needs of high-temperature science.

Future Developments in
the Spectroscopy of High-Temperature Molecules

LEO BREWER

Inorganic Materials Research Division, Lawrence Radiation Laboratory
and Department of Chemistry
University of California
Berkeley, California

Spectroscopy is a powerful tool for high-temperature chemistry.
Characterized spectral lines not only provide means of detection and
quantitative analysis of atoms and molecules in high-temperature
systems such as stars, comets, rocket-exhaust flames, plasmas, and
many other high-temperature vapors, but they also yield valuable information about structures, electronic configurations, and thermodynamic properties of high-temperature molecules. The present paper
reviews some of the current applications of spectroscopy to problems
of high-temperature chemistry, some of the new techniques that have
proved useful or appear promising for the future, and some of the
critical problems of high-temperature chemistry that may be resolved
through the use of spectroscopic techniques.

The first application to be considered deals with atomic spectroscopy, which has in the past been a very important tool for high-
temperature chemistry. Spectroscopic analyses have characterized
the ground electronic states of the atoms as well as the low-lying
electronic states, to an extent sufficient to provide good characterization of the high-temperature thermodynamic properties of a large
fraction of the gaseous elemental atoms. Only for a few lanthanides
and actinides are there substantial uncertainties about thermodynamic
properties at high temperatures because of incompleteness of the
spectroscopic analyses. Active work is continuing on these incomplete
spectra, and, in addition, there is promise of semiempirical approaches that may adequately characterize the low-lying electronic
states and therefore the high-temperature thermodynamic properties.

At this time, I should like to discuss another application of atomic
spectroscopy that provides a good illustration of the varied applications
of spectroscopic data and that also illustrates those areas for which

3

useful spectroscopic data are lacking. Generally, the behavior of chemical substances depends upon the numbers of electrons involved in bonding and upon the character of these electrons, i.e., whether they are of the s, p, d, ... types. Often, the electronic configurations that are important for the bonding of atoms in chemical compounds are not the lowest-lying configurations. An important example of this is the $s^2 p^2\ ^3P$ ground state of carbon. Since the s electrons must be internally paired, only two of the valence electrons of carbon in the ground electronic state are available for bonding. In the typical carbon compounds, such as methane, the bonding is visualized in terms of promotion of the ground electronic configuration to an sp^3 electronic configuration in which all four valence electrons are available for bonding. Considerable energy is required to promote the carbon atom from the ground state to the sp^3 configuration, but the additional bonding energy resulting from two additional bonding electrons more than offsets the promotion energy. The resulting sp^3 configuration gives a characteristic tetrahedral arrangement of the bonding atoms around the carbon.

In metallic systems, one finds (1-3) a similar relationship between the types and numbers of electrons available for bonding and the structure of the metal. The Engel correlation between electronic configurations and crystal structures of metallic systems indicates that electronic configurations involving one s electron produce the body-centered cubic (bcc) structure. Electronic configurations involving an s and a p electron result in the hexagonal close-packed (hcp) structure. Engel has proposed on an empirical basis, and theoretical calculations (4) confirm that mixing varying numbers of d electrons with a single s electron still produces the bcc structure, whereas mixing varying numbers of d electrons with one s and one p electron produces the hcp structure. This correlation has been amply verified (2,3) and has been successfully applied not only to the pure elements but to complex alloy systems. On the basis of this correlation, it becomes possible to use spectroscopic data derived from measurements on the gaseous atoms to predict not only structures but also thermodynamic data for metallic systems.

The application of spectroscopic data for these purposes is illustrated in Figure 1, in which the relative promotion energies of the $d^{n-1}s$ and $d^{n-2}sp$ electronic configurations, where n is the total

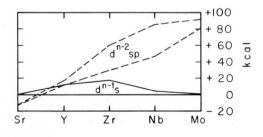

Figure 1. Relative stabilities of $d^{n-1}s$ and d^{n-2} sp electronic configurations for transition metals of the second transition series.

number of valence electrons, are plotted for the transition metals of the second transition series. Both of these configurations have all the valence electrons unpaired and free for bonding. Some differences in bonding ability of d electrons compared with s and p electrons are discussed in detail below, but even if these differences are ignored, we can still use the data shown in Figure 1 to predict qualitatively the relative stability of bcc and hcp structures for these elements. The energies are presented as bands or areas since there are a number of states corresponding to given electronic configurations. The ranges of energies are those of the electronic states of highest multiplicity that correspond to the indicated electronic configurations. It can be seen that for the first three metals—strontium, yttrium, and zirconium—the two configurations lie close enough together in energy that it might be expected that, for these metals, the two structures, bcc ($d^{n-1}s$) and hcp ($d^{n-2}sp$), would also be close together in energy. This is found experimentally to be the case. These three elements all have hcp structures that convert to bcc structures at higher temperatures. Since the bcc structure has a coordination number of 8 compared with a coordination number of 12 for the hcp structure, the bcc phase would be expected to have more vibration and greater entropy and therefore would be the one to become stabilized at the higher temperatures. For niobium and molybdenum, it can be seen that the electronic configuration $d^{n-2}sp$ is so highly promoted compared with the configuration with only one s electron that it can be predicted that the hcp structure would be considerably unstable compared with the bcc structure. This, again, is in agreement with the experimental observations, since only the bcc structure is known for niobium and molybdenum at all temperatures and pressures. Similar comparisons for the other tranisition metals indicate that the predictions that can be made on the basis of available spectroscopic data are in agreement with the available experimental observations. To allow comparison between the predictions of the calculations to be presented below and the experimental observations, the crystal structures of the elements are presented in Table 1.

The spectroscopic data can now be used in a more quantitative manner by using the experimental promotion energies required to achieve each of the two electronic configurations under consideration here, together with the experimental enthalpies of sublimation, to determine the bonding energies that result when the gaseous atoms in the corresponding valence state are condensed to the solid metal. The enthalpies of sublimation of the metals have been taken from published tabulations (2,5). The promotion energies (6) for the $d^{n-2}sp$ electronic configuration are given in Table 2. Table 3 shows the corresponding promotion energies from the ground electronic state of the gaseous atoms to the electronic configuration $d^{n-1}s$. The second numerical entry below each element is the promotion energy that would correspond to the configuration $d^{n-1.5}sp^{0.5}$, which would be the average of the promotion energies for the configuration with one s electron and the configuration with one s and one p electron. The second value is tabulated because the bcc structure is observed up to a total of one and a half electrons per atoms of the s or p type, and thus the range of promotion energies from that for one s electron to that for one and a half s,p electrons must be considered for quantitative treatment of

TABLE 1. Crystal Structures of the Elements[a]

Li I	Be II	B *,*											C IV, [f]	N ≡ [b]	O = [b]	F [c], —
Na I	Mg II	Al III											Si IV	P [e]	S [d]	Cl —
K I	Ca I, II.	Sc I, II	Ti I, II	V I	Cr I	Mn I, III, β, χ	Fe I, III, I	Co III, II	Ni III	Cu III	Zn II	Ga A11	Ge IV	As [e]	Se [d]	Br —
Rb I	Sr I, II, III	Y I, II	Zr I, II	Nb I	Mo I	Tc II	Ru II	Rh III	Pd III	Ag III	Cd II	In (III)[g]	Sn A5, IV	Sb [e]	Te [d]	I —
Cs I	Ba I	La I, III, II	Hf I, II	Ta I	W I	Re II	Os II	Ir III	Pt III	Au III	Hg A10	Tl I, II	Pb III	Bi [e]	Po	At
Fr	Ra	Ac														

Ce	Pr	Nd	Pm	Sm	Eu	Gd	Tb	Dy	Ho	Er	Tm	Yb	Lu
Ce I, III, II	Pr I, II	Nd I, II	Pm	Sm I, (II)[g]	Eu I	Gd I, II	Tb I, II	Dy I, II	Ho I, II	Er I, II	Tm I, II	Yb I, III	Lu I, II
Th I, III	Pa *	U I, σ, (II)	Np I, **	Pu I, *, III, ***	Am ?, II	Cm ?, II	Bk	Cf	Es	Fm	Md		Lw

[a] I. Body-centered cubic, A2. II, Hexagonal close packed, A3. III, Cubic close packed, A1. IV, Diamond, A4. Asterisk denotes complex structure.

[b] Diatomic molecules with double or triple bonds.

[c] Diatomic molecule with a single electron pair bond.

[d] Atoms that form two single bonds per atom to form rings or infinite chains.

[e] Three single bonds per atom, corresponding to a puckered planar structure.

[f] The graphite structure where one resonance form consists of two single and one double bond per atom.

[g] Parentheses indicate slight distortions. The structures are listed in order of temperature stability except for metastable diamond.

TABLE 2. Promotion Energies of $d^{n-2}sp$ Valence State in kcal/mole

Ground-State Configurations[a]

s^2	ds^2	d^2s^2	d^3s^2	d^5s	d^5s^2	d^6s^2	d^7s^2	d^8s^2	$d^{10}s$	$d^{10}s^2$
Mg 63										
Ca 43	Sc 45–46, 53	Ti 45–54, 72–80	V 47–54, 81–88	Cr 71–80	Mn 53	Fe 55–70	Co 67–76	Ni 74–87	Cu 113–128	Zn 92–94
Sr 41–43	Y 43–49, 54	Zr 42–57, 66–74	Nb(d^4s) 48–61, 74–86	Mo 80–93	Tc 47–50	Ru(d^7s) 72–93	Rh(d^8s) (95)–	Pd(d^{10}) <145–	Ag 161–185	Cd 86–91
Ba 35–39	La 38–46, 50–52	Hf 51–79, 85–95	Ta 49–99	W(d^4s^2) 55–85	Re 54–68	Os 67–(90)	Ir 75–109	Pt(d^9s) 86–160	Au 121–160	Hg 108–126
Ra 37–48	Ac 39–68									

[a] As indicated in the column heading, except where otherwise indicated in parentheses.

7

TABLE 3. Promotion Energies of $d^{n-1}s$ and $d^{n-1.5}sp^{0.5}$ Valence States in kcal/mole[a]

Ground-State Configurations[b]

	s^2	ds^2	d^2s^2	d^3s^2	d^5s	d^5s^2	d^6s^2	d^7s^2	d^8s^2	$d^{10}s$
	Mg									
	137									
	100									
	Ca	Sc	Ti	V	Cr	Mn	Fe	Co	Ni	Cu
	58	33, 51	19, 40	6–7	0	49–50	20–23, 50–51	10–15, 43–46	1–5	0
	51	39–43, 48–52	32–60	26–48	36–40	51–52	38–47, 53–61	39–61	37–46	
	Sr	Y	Zr	Nb(d^4s)	Mo	Te	Ru(d^7 s)	Rh(d^8 s)	Pd(d^{10})	Ag
	52	31–33, 44	14–17, 31–32	0–3	0	7–12	0–9, 25–27	0–10, 26–31	19–29	0
	47	37–49	28–53	24–45	40–47	27–31	36–60			
	Ba	La	Hf	Ta	W(d^4 s^2)	Re	Os	Ir	Pt(d^9s)	Au
	26–27	8–12, 21–22	40–51, 59–64	28–38	8	34–49	15–37, 44–(51)	8–34, 37–48	0–29	0
	30–33	23–37	46–79	39–69	32–47	44–58	41–52, 56–	42–78	43–	
	Ra	Ac								
	37–42	(15–20), 26–35								
	38–45	26–51								

[a] The numerical entry below the symbol of an element gives values for the d^{n-1} s valence state. Where a second entry is given, it is for the $d^{n-1.5}sp^{0.5}$ valence state.

[b] As indicated in the column heading, except where otherwise indicated in parentheses.

8

the data for bcc structure. The calculation of stabilities of the bcc structure based on the two configurations is illustrated in Appendix 1 (page 18) and can be used to determine which configuration is more appropriate. Generally, it may be expected that throughout the periodic table the bonding energies of s or p electrons decrease with increasing internuclear distances as one goes down in the periodic table. One would expect the bonding energies to increase to the right in the periodic table because of increasing nuclear charge. Figure 2 illustrates data for bonding energies of metals of the second transition series. The curve labeled 5 s,p shows how the bonding energy due to an s or p electron varies in going from Sr to Cd. The values for Sr and Cd can be fixed directly since they both have hcp structures corresponding to sp electronic configurations. The interpolated smooth curve connecting these values represents the expected variation of bonding energy as nuclear charge is increased. For each of the elements in this series, the total bonding energy was calculated from the combination of sublimation enthalpies and promotion energies. The contribution of the s or p electrons was subtracted, the number of s and p electrons being determined by the structure. The remaining bonding energy was assigned to the remaining d electrons, and the curves labeled 4d in Figure 2 correspond to the bonding energy per d electron available for bonding (i.e., the remaining bonding energy divided by the number of unpaired d electrons). The characteristic curves shown here are typical of the curves found for the other transition series in that the bonding effectiveness of a d electron decreases as the number of d bonds increases, reaching a minimum at the maximum of five d bonds per atom, apparently due to interference among the d bonds when there are too large a number of d bonds. The x's indicate the experimental points derived from hcp structures; the circles indicate the values derived from bcc structures. The bonding energy of an electron is largely independent of the particular structure, and one can draw a

Figure 2. Bonding energies per electron for s,p, and d electrons of metals of second transition series.

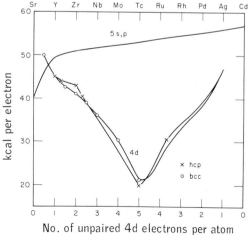

TABLE 4. Bonding Energies of the $d^{n-2}sp$ Valence State in the Hexagonal Close-Packed Structure[a]

Number of Bonding Electrons Per Atom

2	3	4	5	6	7	6	5	4	2.4	2
In kcal/mole										
Mg 98										
Ca (84)	Sc 136	Ti 158	V (165)	Cr (158)	Mn (121)	Fe 154	Co 169	Ni (171)	Cu* (135)	Zn 124
Sr 80	Y 144	Zr 188	Nb* (197)	Mo* (198)	Tc 205	Ru* 205	Rh* (189)	Pd* (165)	Ag* (130)	Cd 114
Ba (74)	La 142	Hf 198	Ta (230)	W (244)	Re 241	Os 255	Ir (234)	Pt (215)	Au* (140)	Hg (123)
In kcal/bonding electron										
Mg 49										
Ca (42)	Sc 45	Ti 40	V (33)	Cr (26)	Mn (17)	Fe 26	Co 34	Ni (43)	Cu* (56)	Zn 62
Sr 40	Y 48	Zr 47	Nb* (39)	Mo* (33)	Tc 29	Ru* 38	Rh* (43)	Pd* (49)	Ag* (54)	Cd 57
Ba (37)	La 47	Hf 50	Ta (46)	W (41)	Re 34	Os 43	Ir (47)	Pt (54)	Au* (58)	Hg (62)

[a] Asterisks indicate that bonding energy is given for the $d^{n-1.7}sp^{0.7}$ valence state. The number of bonding electrons per atom for Ru*, Rh*, and Pd* are, respectively, 5.4, 4.4, and 3.4. For Cu*, Ag*, and Au*, the $d^{9.3}sp^{0.7}$ valence state has 2.4 bonding electrons per atom.

10

curve that can be used for predicting the bonding in yet unobserved phases of these metals with either the bcc or hcp structures. For example, for hcp niobium, which has never been observed, one could predict the stability of such a phase by calculating the bonding energy that would result from the configuration d^3sp if the bonding energies given in Figure 2 for an s or p electron of niobium were multiplied by 2 and if the bonding energy for a d electron when there are a total of three d bonds per atom, as indicated by the ordinate at the bottom of Figure 2, were multiplied by 3. This bonding energy for three d electrons, added to the contribution of the two sp electrons, yields the total bonding energy for the valence state d^3sp, condensing to produce hcp niobium. From this bonding energy must now be subtracted the promotion energy given in Table 2 for the configuration d^3sp, to yield an atomization energy of 158 kcal for hcp niobium. A similar procedure for the configuration d^4s yields a bonding energy of 173 kcal for the bcc structure, indicating that the hcp structure of niobium is unstable by 15 kcal.

This procedure has been carried out for all the transition metals, and Table 4 presents the bonding energies when the indicated valence states of the gaseous atoms are combined to form hcp solids. Table 5 shows the corresponding bonding energies for the formation of bcc structures. These can then be combined with the promotion energies given previously to calculate the heats of sublimation of either bcc or hcp structures for all the transition metals, although the calculations for the hcp phases of rhodium and palladium are less accurate since the spectroscopic data for the $d^{n-2}sp$ configurations are incomplete or lacking for these two elements.

Thus, we have here an illustration of how the gaseous atomic spectroscopic observations can be used to provide thermodynamic data for phases that are metastable and that might be prepared under suitable conditions. For example, hcp Fe is unstable with respect to bcc Fe by 1 kcal, but the hcp phase is considerably more dense than the bcc phase and it is possible to produce it at high pressures. In other cases, the metastable phases may be produced by reduction of suitable compounds at sufficiently low temperatures or even by quenching from the liquid phase. The bcc structure in particular, with its lower coordination number, might well be favored by rapid quenching of the liquid phases of metals that would normally form close-packed structures. In addition to allowing the prediction of which structures should be stable for the pure elements and of the degree of instability of the unstable structures, the spectroscopic data can also be used for predicting the high-temperature behavior of complex alloy mixtures of these metals (2). In principle, similar calculations can be carried out for the face-centered cubic structure, but the spectroscopic data are very incomplete for the electronic configurations required for the face-centered cubic structure, and many

TABLE 5. Bonding Energies of the $d^{n-1}s$ or $d^{n-1.5}sp^{0.5}$ Valence States in the Body-Centered Cubic Structure

Valence State and Number of Bonding Electrons Per Atom[a]

1	2	3	4	5	6	6	5	4	3	2	1
s	$d^{0.5}sp^{0.5}$	$d^{1.5}sp^{0.5}$	$d^{2.5}sp^{0.5}$	$d^{3.5}sp^{0.5}$	$d^5 s$	$d^{5.5}sp^{0.5}$	$d^{6.5}sp^{0.5}$	$d^{7.5}sp^{0.5}$	$d^{7.5}sp^{0.5}$	$d^9 s$	$d^{10}s$
In kcal/mole											
Na 26											
K 21.5	Ca 92	Sc 129	Ti 144	V 149	Cr($d^{4.5}sp^{0.5}$) 131	Mn 119	Fe 138	Co (139)	Ni (135)		Cu (61)
Rb 19.5	Sr 85	Y 138	Zr 174	Nb(d^4s) 173	Mo 157	Tc (179)		Ru(d^7s) (153)	Rh(d^8s) (131)	Pd (102)	Ag (56)
Cs 19	Ba 73	La 126	Hf 192	Ta 226	W 211	Re (228)	Os (218)	Ir (197)	Pt (167)		Au (59)
In kcal/bonding electron											
Na 26											
K 22	Ca 46	Sc 43	Ti 36	V 30	Cr 22	Mn 20	Fe 28	Co (35)	Ni (45)		Cu (61)
Rb 20	Sr 43	Y 46	Zr 44	Nb 35	Mo 26	Tc (30)		Ru (38)	Rh (44)	Pd (51)	Ag (56)
Cs 19	Ba 37	La 42	Hf 48	Ta 45	W 35	Re (38)	Os (44)	Ir (49)	Pt (56)		Au (59)

[a] As indicated in the column heading, except where otherwise indicated in parentheses.

extrapolations and estimates must be made for detailed calculations as illustrated elsewhere (3). Thus, the extension of the analyses of the spectra of atoms to higher electronic configurations would be very valuable in allowing the extension of calculations of this type to other structures.

In the time available, it would be impossible to illustrate the many applications of molecular spectroscopy, and I will cite only several examples of new techniques in this field. In contrast to the situation for the gaseous atoms, the characterization of the ground states and low-lying electronic states of most high-temperature molecules is very incomplete. Even for the diatomic molecules, the ground states have been characterized only for a relatively small fraction of molecules of interest. This is due in part to the much greater complexity of molecular spectra compared with atomic spectra. For each electronic transition, there are a large number of lines corresponding to rotational and vibrational excitations. The overlapping of this multitude of lines from different electronic configurations often makes the analyses extremely difficult.

The high-temperature molecules pose a particular problem. When one is dealing with a molecule that can be produced in a gaseous state at low temperatures, it is relatively easy to determine the ground state in an absorption experiment at low temperatures where any absorption could come only from the ground state. In a high-temperature system, the observation of a band system in absorption does not demonstrate that the absorbing level is the ground state since low-lying states may be sufficiently populated to give strong absorption. The determination of the correct ground state makes a quite substantial difference in the thermodynamic properties. As an illustration, one might consider diatomic MgO, where a question exists as to whether the ground state is a singlet sigma state or a triplet pi state. Because of degeneracy of the $^3\Pi$ state by a factor of 6 and a greater contribution to the entropy by vibration and rotation, the partition function calculated on the basis of a possible $^3\Pi$ state might be a factor of 10 greater than that based on a $^1\Sigma$ state. The calculated equilibrium concentration of MgO based on a $^3\Pi$ ground state and a heat formation obtained by a second-law method, for example, would yield an equilibrium concentration ten times higher than that calculated on the basis of a $^1\Sigma$ state.

A detailed discussion of application of molecular orbital correlations to prediction of missing low-lying electronic states is given in an earlier paper (7). It is difficult to obtain experimental demonstrations of these missing levels. I wish to discuss briefly some techniques that we have been using at Berkeley to attempt to resolve this problem. One of these methods is the production of a molecular beam of the molecule in question and observation of the absorption spectrum of the molecular beam. For heavy molecules for which spin prohibitions are not severe, it is to be expected that virtually all excited electronic states will decay to the ground state in a period of time on the order of 10^{-4} to 10^{-3} sec. Such transit times for a molecular beam can be obtained. The procedure then is to produce the molecular beam in some high-temperature Knudsen cell and to examine its absorption spectrum at a sufficient distance from the orifice of the Knudsen cell. Comparison of the observed absorption spectrum with known spectra will then establish the character of the ground state. Normally, there is not sufficient optical density in the molecular beam to obtain a strong absorption spectrum, but spectra have been obtained through the use of multiple reflections across the beam. A simpler method that is equivalent to the absorption experiment is the excitation of a fluorescent spectrum using a light source at the wavelength of the fluorescent light. A recent example of the successful use of this method involved the LaO molecule (8). Known bands of LaO were excited in fluorescence by illumination of the molecular beam by a tungsten light source. Filters were then used to eliminate any light on the violet side of these fluorescent bands. No change in intensity was observed, which demonstrates that all the fluorescent light resulted from absorption from the ground state to the upper state and return to the ground state. This method should be applicable to many of the heavier molecules.

Another procedure involves the entrapment of high-temperature molecules in a noble gas or other inert matrix at liquid-hydrogen or liquid-helium temperatures. A number of laboratories in the United States have used this method to trap a variety of high-temperature molecules. It proves possible in many instances to observe not only the absorption spectrum due to either electronic transitions or infrared vibrational transitions, but also to observe fluorescent spectra. Thus, for S_2 it was possible to obtain information about vibrational levels of both the ground state and the excited electronic state (9,10). There is some expectation that this method might be applicable to the observation of weak intercombination bands not easily seen in the gas due to the breakdown of selection rules by the environment of the matrix. In some instances, the technique may be useful for the synthesis of high-temperature molecules that can be produced only with difficulty in high-temperature systems without contamination by other molecular species. For example, it is hoped that diatomic MgO can be produced readily by entrapment of magnesium atoms and oxygen atoms in a noble-gas matrix; reaction would then follow upon a slight increase in temperature that would allow diffusion of the atoms to form diatomic molecules. The process would have to be very carefully controlled to avoid production of more-complex species. The matrix-isolation technique has the advantage of removing excess vibrational excitation and therefore simplifying spectra compared with those obtained

from high-temperature sources, but it has the disadvantage of intro-
ducing complexities into the spectrum due to matrix interactions.

In many instances, the search for low-lying electronic levels of
high-temperature molecules has proved extremely difficult because
the desired states do not combine at high intensity with states that
would yield spectra in readily accessible spectral regions. There are
indications that studying of perturbations in known band systems may
be a fruitful way of characterizing electronic states that have not been
observed directly. This method, combined with isotopic substitutions,
may in many instances be the most convenient way of fixing the positions of the low-lying electronic states.

Another procedure that shows some promise also deals with molecular beams. When a molecular beam is excited in fluorescence by a
light source at right angles to the molecular beam, the resulting fluorescent light will be polarized, even if the exciting light is not polarized,
because of unequal population of Zeeman levels of the molecule. The
degree of polarization will depend upon the change in rotational quantum number such that Q lines with no change in rotational quantum
number will be more highly polarized than P or R lines. This may be
a useful method of at least characterizing the change in orbital angular
momentum for spectra that have not been rotationally analyzed.

There are a variety of other molecular-beam techniques that should
prove useful. One example is the molecular-beam electric-deflection
method used by Klemperer (11,12) to characterize molecules in molecular beams. The question of whether these techniques are useful for
obtaining information about states other than the ground states, at least
for the heavier molecules, depends upon the extent to which excited
electronic states can persist in the molecular beam. For heavier molecules, for which the coupling approaches case c and for which all transitions are formally allowed except those involving a change in omega
greater than 1 or those between O^- and O^+ states, there is a good
chance that all states will decay to the ground state before the beam
has reached the detector. For some of the heavier molecules, the
effect of case c coupling is to cause substantial splitting of the sublevels. The example of I_2 is, of course, well known: the $^3\Pi$ state arising from the promotion of an electron in a filled π orbital to the next
excited σ orbital has $^3\Pi_0$ and $^3\Pi_1$ components separated by 3,800 cm^{-1}.
Some of the substates are repulsive and some attractive. Another re-
cent example of the wide separation of sublevels is that of Se_2, which
has been recently analyzed by Brown (13) at Oxford University. The
ground state of Se_2 has been recorded as a $^1\Sigma$ ground state in the past,
in contrast to the $^3\Sigma^-$ state predicted from the molecular orbital theory.
Barrow has shown that in fact the Se_2 ground state is $^3\Sigma^-$, but actually
the state is so far toward case c coupling that it has split into an O^+ and
a 1 level, which are separated by several hundred cm^{-1}. Over part of

the spectral range, the 1 state has been predissociated so that one sees only a O - O transition that had been characterized as a $^1\Sigma$ - $^1\Sigma$ transition. Indications are that for Te_2 as for I_2, the separations are even larger. When the energy difference between sublevels becomes large, the probability of emission from one sublevel to the other is increased. When these emission lifetimes become 10^{-3} sec or shorter, molecular-beam techniques may yield misleading results since only molecules at the lowest sublevel will reach the detector. Also, the analysis of ordinary optical spectra may be misleading in that transitions involving different sublevels of states of higher multiplicity may be analyzed as separate systems and designated as singlets, as in the example of Se_2 cited above. This raises the question of whether other states that have been reported as singlet states actually might be sublevels of triplet states. An interesting example is reported by Trajmar and Ewing [14] for MgO, where a $^1\Sigma^-$ state has been characterized by the transition to the lower $^1\Pi$ state of MgO, where a $^1\Delta$ state 229 cm^{-1} away has been found to have virtually the same molecular constants. This would seem to indicate that instead of being singlet states, they may in fact be sublevels of a $^3\Pi$ state, with the $^1\Delta$ corresponding to $^3\Pi_2$ and the $^1\Sigma^-$ corresponding to $^3\Pi_0$. These examples indicate the difficulty of clearly characterizing some of the spectral data.

The alkaline earths, in particular, illustrate the difficulties of characterizing molecular spectroscopic data when the data are incomplete. A number of alkaline earth oxides and sulfides have been studied by mass-spectrometer techniques, flame equilibria, and other methods [15]. Most of these measurements indicate a partition function ranging between 5 and 10 for these states. The lowest states that have been seen in analyzed spectra have been $^1\Sigma$ states, although Barrow [16] has seen triplet systems of BeS in absorption. Klemperer has shown that for BaO and SrO, the lowest ground state is a nondegenerate state, either $^1\Sigma^+$ or $^3\Pi_0^+$. On the other hand, unless there are serious unexpected experimental errors in some of the equilibrium studies, it would appear that there are low-lying states adding substantially to the partition function. This problem has been studied with all the conventional techniques and with a few of the newer techniques, but it still has not been resolved. It is clear that additional and novel methods will be needed before this important problem can be resolved.

The situation is definitely worse for the more-complex molecules. An illustration of the difficulties can be given in the example of C_3. The thermodynamic properties of C_3 have been determined by a number of vaporization studies, which have established the thermodynamic properties by second- and third-law methods. On the other hand, the determination of the bending frequency of C_3 by Herzberg and his group [17] leads to a severe contradiction between the equilibrium results and the partition function calculated from the spectroscopic data. The spectroscopic data are incomplete in that the observed bending frequency, which is the major contributor to the partition function, has been characterized only up to $v'' = 4$. At very high temperature, many vibrational levels are excited. The spacing of the levels observed seems to open up with increasing vibrational excitation. It is possible that the contradiction can be resolved if the spacing continues to open up rapidly enough so that the bulk of the levels that contribute to the high-temperature partition function are actually separated by much larger energy intervals than are the first few levels characterized. Attempts to treat the observed data by a quartic function (18) to predict the extent to which the higher vibrational levels might open up removes about half of the discrepancy, but there still is a very large difference remaining. In this particular example, there appears to be no question about the linear structure of the ground state. However, in some of the more-complex high-temperature molecules, such as Mo_3O_9, there are no data available to give any indication of what the structure might be. Molecular-beam electric-deflection methods, the type used by Büchler et al. (19), together with a mass spectrometer, might be of use here in at least determining the symmetry of the molecule. However, there seem to be no methods in prospect for characterizing the detailed structures of these molecules.

Another new technique that should prove useful for study of the ground states of some molecules has been used by Berkowitz at the Argonne Laboratories and by Blue and Meschi at Berkeley; they combine a Stern-Gerlach experiment with a mass spectrometer to determine whether or not a high-temperature vapor contains triplet states. This method, like some of the other molecular-beam methods discussed earlier, may not be applicable to heavy molecules due to the decay of low-lying electronic states and even of sublevels of the ground states. For example, it is possible that in a molecular beam of Se_2 or Te_2 the 1 sublevel of the $^3\Sigma^-$ ground state may emit radiation going to the O^+ sublevel and thus behave as a $^1\Sigma^+$ state in the Stern-Gerlach experiment. It would be very valuable to know the lifetimes of these sublevels to determine what limitations there might be on the use of molecular beam techniques for heavy molecules.

This work was performed under the auspices of the United States Atomic Energy Commission.

REFERENCES

1. L. Brewer, "Thermodynamic Stability and Bond Character in Relation to Electronic Structure and Crystal Structure," in Electronic Structure and Alloy Chemistry and Crystal Structure, P. A. Beck, ed., Interscience, New York (1963), Dover, New York (1965), pp. 221-235.
2. L. Brewer, "Prediction of High Temperature Metallic Phase Diagrams," in High-Strength Materials, V. F. Zackay, ed., Wiley, New York (1965), pp. 12-103.

3. L. Brewer, "Viewpoints on Stability of Metallic Structures," paper presented at "Colloquium on Phase Stability in Metals and Alloys," Geneva and Villars, Switzerland, March 7-12, 1966.

4. S. L. Altman, C. A. Coulson, and W. Hume-Rothery, Proc. Roy. Soc., A240, 145 (1957).

5. R. Hultgren, R. L. Orr, P. D. Anderson, and K. K. Kelley, Selected Values for the Thermodynamic Properties of Metals and Alloys, Wiley, New York (1963) and Supplement (1965).

6. C. E. Moore, Atomic Energy Levels, Volumes 1-3, U.S. Govt. Printing Office, Washington, D.C. (1949, 1952, 1958).

7. L. Brewer, Proc. Robert A. Welch Foundation Conf. Chem. Res., 6, 47 (1963).

8. L. Brewer and R. M. Walsh, J. Chem. Phys., 42, 4055 (1965).

9. L. Brewer, G. D. Brabson, and B. Meyer, J. Chem. Phys., 42, 1385 (1965).

10. L. Brewer and G. D. Brabson, J. Chem. Phys., in press.

11. L. Wharton, M. Kaufman, and W. Klemperer, J. Chem. Phys., 37, 622 (1962); 39, 240 (1963).

12. L. Wharton, R. A. Berg, and W. Klemperer, J. Chem. Phys., 39, 2023 (1963).

13. G. G. Chandler, R. F. Barrow, and C. B. Meyer, Philosophical Trans. Roy. Soc., in press.

14. S. Trajmar and G. E. Ewing, Astrophys. J., 142, 77 (1965).

15. L. Brewer and G. M. Rosenblatt, review paper on diatomic oxides, in preparation.

16. C. J. Cheetham, W. J. M. Gissane, and R. F. Barrow, Trans. Faraday Soc., 61, 1308 (1965).

17. L. Gausset, G. Herzberg, A. Lagerqvist, and B. Rosen, Disc. Faraday Soc., 35, 113 (1963); Astrophys. J., 142, 45 (1965).

18. A. G. Robiette and H. L. Strauss, University of California, manuscript to be published.

19. A. Büchler, J. L. Stauffer, and W. Klemperer, J. Chem. Phys., 41, 3471 (1964).

APPENDIX 1

Sample Calculation of Bonding Electronic Configuration in a Metal

Molybdenum is used as an example. For bcc Mo, the configurations d^5s and $d^{4.5} sp^{0.5}$ represent the extreme electronic ranges. From Figure 2 (page 7) the bonding energy for the d^5s valence state is 52 + (5 x 21) or 157 kcal; the promotion energy is zero. Thus, the atomization energy is 157 kcal. For the $d^{4.5} sp^{0.5}$ valence state, the bonding energy from Figure 2 is (1.5 x 52) + (4.5 x 25) or 190.5 kcal. The promotion energy from Table 3 (page 8) 40 kcal; the atomization energy is 150 kcal. Thus, the correct bonding configuration for bcc Mo is d^5s.

For hcp Mo, the extremes are $d^{4.3} sp^{0.7}$ and $d^4 sp$. The calculations are (1.7 x 52) + (4.3 x 25.5) = 198; subtracting 56 kcal of promotion energy yields an atomization energy of 142 kcal and, similarly, (2 x 52) + (4 x 27) = 212, less 80 yields 132, respectively. Thus, the configuration $d^{4.3} sp^{0.7}$, at the lower s,p concentration range of the hcp structure, has the more stable structure. The hcp phase of Mo is metastable by 15 kcal (i.e., 157 - 142 kcal).

Applications of Molecular-Beam Techniques to High-Temperature Chemistry

MYRON KAUFMAN
Department of Chemistry
Harvard University
Cambridge, Massachusetts

Recent developments in molecular-beam spectroscopic and deflection experiments have provided important information concerning the geometric and electronic structures of simple molecules of interest to the high-temperature chemist. Molecular-beam techniques are well suited for the study of refractory or unstable species because, in a molecular beam, molecules contact the apparatus only at the beam source and detector. Thus, we have been able to generate beams of BaO, SrO, and LaO by heating tungsten and iridium ovens to temperatures as high as $2,500\,^{\circ}$K. Excited states with appreciable Boltzmann factors at these high temperatures can also be investigated in molecular beams, provided that the molecule does not spontaneously decay from this state during its transit time in the beam. States up to 4,000 cm^{-1} above the ground state may be accessible for study by this method. Higher-energy metastable states, for example, A $^3\Pi$ of CO, have been populated in beams by exciting molecules with electron bombardment. Attempts are also being made to generate beams of chemically unstable species, such as the free radical CH, by obtaining the beam from a suitable position in a fast-flow reactor. Flames and discharges are examples of systems that could be sampled in this manner.

Because effective pressures in molecular beams are only of the order of 10^{-13} torr, it is advantageous to use a method of detection that is specific for the species of interest. One such method, specific for metastable states such as the A $^3\Pi$ of CO, involves ejection of electrons from a surface by the Auger effect. Another employs surface ionization and detects only molecules containing an atom of low ionization potential. Detection by electron-bombardment ionization followed by mass-spectrometric analyses of the ions is applicable to all molecules. However, because of this nonspecificity, it is necessary to maintain a very low background pressure in the ionizing region. It is also important to achieve high ionization efficiency in order to reduce the shot noise resulting from the statistics of counting individual ions. A new electron bombardment ionizer in our laboratory forms one ion from 10^2-10^3 incoming beam particles and will operate at a background pressure of less than 10^{-9} torr.

Inhomogeneous electric and magnetic fields are used to deflect beams of molecules. In an electric quadrupole field, polar molecules in certain (J, M_J) states experience a radial force toward the beam axis; nonpolar molecules do not show this effect. Such a field has been used to distinguish between linear and bent configurations for a large number of MX_2 triatomic molecules. The behavior of polar <u>diatomic</u> molecules in a quadrupole field depends on whether the molecules have a first- or second-order Stark effect. For a second-order effect, spatial focusing is achieved; for a first-order effect, the molecules experience a larger force at any given field gradient. Since a first-order Stark effect requires a degenerate electronic state, focusing behavior in electric quadrupole fields can distinguish between nondegenerate Σ states and doubly degenerate Π, Δ, ... states of diatomic molecules. This method has been used to determine that the ground electronic state of LiO is Π and that the ground electronic state of LaO is Σ. Electrostatic <u>dipole</u> fields linearly deflect molecules to the right or left of the beam axis depending upon the sign of their effective electric dipole moment. Our present configuration for electric resonance experiments employs a quadrupole field to increase the aperture of the system by spatial focusing and a dipole field to allow the beam to be deflected off-axis in order to achieve high selectivity and to reduce scattered beam reaching the detector.

Inhomogeneous magnetic fields can be used to indicate the presence of molecules in paramagnetic states in beams, since the effective magnetic moments are much larger in such states than in $^1\Sigma$ states. In some paramagnetic electronic states the electronic magnetic moment is coupled to the internuclear axis and considerably reduced by the rapid rotation of the molecule at high temperatures. However, the average effective magnetic moment of these paramagnetic molecules is still much larger than that of $^1\Sigma$ molecules, where it is the resultant only of rotational magnetic moments, nuclear moments, and diamagnetic susceptibility. This effect has been used to demonstrate that BaO has no paramagnetic states within several thousand cm^{-1} of its ground $^1\Sigma$ state.

Molecular-beam resonance spectroscopy has been performed from several kc/sec to almost 100 gc/sec. The low power-level needed to induce molecular-beam microwave transitions allows these transitions to be quickly located by using a frequency-broadened microwave generator. Double resonance methods (rf and microwave) have been useful in identifying transitions. The high resolution of the resonance method, resulting from the elimination of pressure broadening and first-order Doppler broadening, allows the measurement of nuclear spin - spin and spin - rotation interactions.

The properties measured by molecular-beam resonance spectroscopy have provided experimental tests of theoretically calculated wave functions. Recent self-consistent field calculations on LiF and LiH have obtained electric dipole moments within 0.2 percent of our measured values. In high-temperature molecular-beam experiments, the properties of excited vibrational states of molecules can be measured. Due to bond anharmonicity, the average value of the internuclear distance increases with increasing vibrational quantum number. Measurements in several vibrational states can therefore provide information about the variation of the electronic wave function of a molecule with internuclear distance. For example, the electric dipole moment of BaO has been found to increase with increasing internuclear distance, while for SrO, a very similar molecule, the electric dipole moment decreases with increasing internuclear distance. In the A $^3\Pi$ state of CO, the electric dipole moment shows no measurable variation in the first four vibrational states.

Rotational magnetic moments and nuclear spin - rotation interactions of $^1\Sigma$ molecules arise from the molecular rotation perturbing the $^1\Sigma$ ground-state wave function and producing electronic angular momentum in this state. The mixing in of excited states is inversely proportional to their excitation above the ground state. The magnitude of the rotational magnetic moment and spin - rotation interaction thus indicates whether there are any low-lying states that give large contributions to the perturbation sum. For BaO, the measured value of the rotational magnetic moment, $g_J = 0.103$ nuclear magnetons, indicates that in this molecule there are no excited states with $\Omega = 1$ below about 10,000 cm^{-1} above the ground $^1\Sigma$ state.

High-Temperature Molecules

WILLIAM WELTNER, Jr.
Union Carbide Research Institute
Tarrytown, New York

The high-temperature domain is arbitrarily defined to include the inorganic molecules vaporizing from solids at temperatures near $1,000°$K and higher and the molecules appearing in arcs and in stars at temperatures up to $6,000°$K. The need for detailed information concerning these molecules stems from the importance of molecular properties in the calculation of thermodynamic or kinetic processes involved in the vaporization of refractory materials, the reactions of gases with such materials, and the atmospheres of the cooler stars. Most of this information must be obtained from spectroscopic studies which are incomplete principally because of the difficulties encountered in high-temperature investigations.

DIATOMICS

Some of the more important molecules from the point of view of the technologist and the astrophysicist are derived from the transition metals, which are themselves so vital to high temperature. Table 1 gives the diatomic oxides of primary interest along with the designation of their known or predicted ground electronic states. (Those molecules above the heavy line have been identified in stellar atmospheres.) There is renewed interest in these oxides both theoretically (1) and experimentally (3), and good progress is presently being made in clarifying their electronic properties. Current problems involve the extension of the theoretical work beyond the first row in Table 1 — the first row elements already require considerable computer time — and

TABLE 1. Diatomic Transition-Metal Oxides

ScO	TiO	VO[a]	CrO[a]
$^2\Sigma(\sigma)$	$^3\Delta_r(\delta\sigma)$	$^4\underline{\Sigma(\delta^2\sigma)}$	$^3\underline{\Sigma^-(\delta^2)}$
YO	ZrO	NbO	MoO
$^2\Sigma(\sigma)$	$^1\Sigma^+(\sigma^2)$	$^2\Delta_r(\sigma^2\delta)$	$^3\underline{\Sigma^-(\delta^2)}$
LaO	HfO	TaO	WO
$^2\Sigma(\sigma)$	$^1\underline{\Sigma^+(\sigma^2)}$	$^2\Delta_r(\sigma^2\delta)$	$^3\underline{\Sigma^-(\delta^2)}$

The ground states and configurations underlined are predicted.

[a] Taken from reference 1. ESR studies (2) corroborate the calculated ground state for VO.

the experimental determination of the energies of low-lying excited electronic states.

The diatomic rare-earth oxides, CeO to LuO, are the next immediate problem. They vaporize from the solid oxides, which are very refractory and therefore of interest as high-temperature materials (4). In examining the spectroscopic data on these diatomic molecules, one is struck by the dearth of information: no electronic states have been identified nor bond distances determined. The complexity of their spectra is, of course, the reason. These remarks apply equally well to UO and ThO.*

The alkaline-earth oxides, MgO, SrO, and BaO, have been the subject of several recent investigations (5). That their ground states are $^1\Sigma^+$ now seems to be agreed upon by all workers.

POLYATOMICS

It must be remembered that the concentrations of molecules determined at the pressures of 10^{-6} atm in mass-spectrometry work will change at higher pressures so that the larger molecules may become relatively more important as vaporization products (6). There is also

* Some recent spectroscopic work on ThO has been done by M. J. Linevsky in the papers referred to in reference 3.

increasing evidence that polyatomic molecules, other than C_3 and SiC_2, may be present in stellar atmospheres (7).

The triatomic oxides, MO_2, of many of the elements in Table 1 and of U and Th have been observed by mass spectrometry and to some extent by optical spectroscopy (3), but their electronic properties and molecular structures are not established, although in a few cases vibrational frequencies have been determined. Even less information is available on CeO_2, PrO_2, and TbO_2, which have been identified among the rare-earth oxide vapors. The corresponding carbides, MC_2, particularly of U and Th, have also not been investigated spectroscopically.

A great variety of molecules, such as WO_3, W_2O_6, W_3O_8, W_3O_9, and higher polymers, are formed in the oxidation of W and, similarly, in the oxidation of Mo. These require study, since almost all their properties are a matter of conjecture. The tungsten oxide molecules have been trapped in solid neon (8) at $4°K$ and some of their vibrational frequencies have been determined, but much remains to be done. The oxidation of such metals is of obvious practical importance.

Carbon vaporizes to C_3, C, C_2, C_4, C_5, at temperatures near $2,500°K$, where the order given is that of decreasing contribution to the total vapor pressure. Although the properties of C_3 have recently been considerably clarified, most notably by the observation of an extremely low-bending frequency of 63 cm^{-1} in the ground state (9), there still remains a large discrepancy between third-law and careful second-law measurements (10). A large negative anharmonicity in the bending mode of C_3 contributes to this discrepancy.* The importance of C_3, not only as the major contributor to carbon vapor but also in stars and comets, dictates the need for further work. The C_4, C_5, and larger molecules are relatively unimportant at 1 atm pressure, but will become important at higher pressures near the triple point of about $4,000°K$. Theoretical work has indicated what sort of properties these polymers may have (11), and they have been prepared in matrices at $4°K$ (10), but the information about them is tenuous.

Similar polymers of silicon and carbon exist in the vapor over solid silicon carbide. SiC_2 (observed in cool carbon stars), Si_2C, and Si_2C_3 are present and some of their vibrational properties are known (12), but their spectra under high resolution have not been obtained or have not been analyzed. Other long-chain molecules of interest are the hydrocarbon fragments such as C_2H, C_3H, and C_3H_2. They are important as intermediates in the carbon - hydrogen system in shock tubes (13), plasmas (13), and probably in stars (7). Related to these are the nitrogen-substituted radicals C_2N (15), C_3N, and others (7). Further detailed molecular orbital calculations along the carbon polymer lines are needed for all these larger species.

*See references 9 and 10; calculations of the effect of this anharmonicity on the thermodynamic properties of C_3 have recently been carried out by H. L. Strauss (private communication).

NUMBERS

The transition probabilities or oscillator strengths (f numbers) of high-temperature molecules are essentially unknown, so the determination of the concentrations of molecules, particularly in stars, from spectroscopic measurements is very approximate. Further work is required in this area.

TECHNIQUES

The observation of the vapors over refractory solids when under high pressure of inert gas, or a simulation of such a condition, is needed. The purpose is to observe the larger molecules which only appear in high concentration in the saturated vapor at high pressures and temperatures. One would like to know, for example, what molecules are present in the vapor over carbon at its triple point at about 100 atm and $4,000\,^\circ$K.

The spectroscopy of shock-excited powdered solids has been shown to be a promising area (16), but there has been little exploitation of this technique. Variation of the applied shock allows the effective temperature to be varied so that molecular or atomic species can be observed in emission or absorption.

The study of high-temperature molecules trapped in solid inert gases at $4\,^\circ$K (i.e., utilizing matrix isolation techniques) continues to give valuable information. Both optical and ESR spectroscopy can be applied to establish the ground electronic state and the vibrational frequencies in many electronic levels. ESR has so far been applied only to ScO, YO, LaO (17) and VO (18). The recent discovery that molecules can be preferentially oriented in matrices relative to the condensing substrate will make this an even more powerful tool (2).* Figure 1 shows the design of the EPR apparatus in which this work was done; it is modeled after that of Jen et al. (19). Effort is also being made to see whether spectroscopic investigation of matrices can provide f numbers and can lead to the location of low-lying electronic states of high-temperature molecules.

We have omitted any discussion of the metallic halides and of the molecules formed by the lighter elements which appear in rocket exhausts. These present a corresponding range of problems for the high-temperature chemist.

---

* A more complete description of the apparatus and results on CuF_2 and $Cu(NO_3)_2$ is soon to be published.

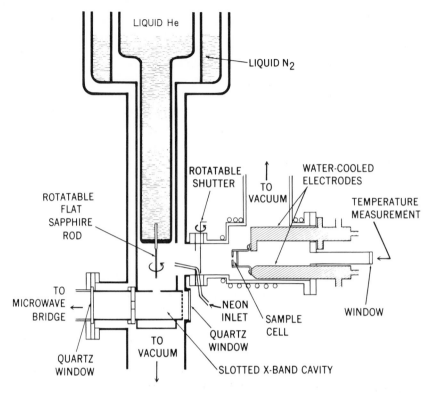

Figure 1. EPR apparatus for the study of high-temperature molecules (2). The sapphire rod, on which the matrix is prepared, can be lowered into the microwave cavity.

REFERENCES

1. TiO: K. D. Carlson and C. Moser, J. Phys. Chem., 67, 2644 (1963); K. D. Carlson and R. K. Nesbet, J. Chem. Phys., 41, 1051 (1964). ScO: K. D. Carlson, E. Ludēna, and C. Moser, J. Chem. Phys., 43, 2408 (1965). VO: K. D. Carlson and C. Moser, in press. CrO: K. D. Carlson and C. Moser, tentative calculations.
2. P. H. Kasai, W. Weltner, Jr., and E. B. Whipple, J. Chem. Phys., 42, 1120 (1965).
3. ScO, YO, LaO: R. A. Berg, L. Wharton, W. Klemperer, A. Büchler, and J. L. Stauffer, J. Chem. Phys., 43, 2416 (1965); L. Brewer and R. M. Walsh, J. Chem. Phys., 42, 4055 (1965); P. H. Kasai and W. Weltner, Jr., J. Chem. Phys., 43, 2553 (1965). TiO, ZrO, HfO: M. J. Linevsky, Proc. Meeting Interagency Chem. Rocket Propulsion Group Thermochem., 1st, New York 1, 11 (1964), and 3rd, El Segundo, California 1, 71 (1965), Chemical Propulsion Information Agency, The Johns Hopkins Applied Physics Laboratory, Silver Spring, Md.; W. Weltner, Jr., and D. McLeod, Jr., J. Phys. Chem., 69, 3488 (1965). TaO and TaO$_2$: W. Weltner, Jr., and

D. McLeod, Jr., J. Chem. Phys., 42, 882 (1965). WO and WO_2: W. Weltner and D. McLeod, Jr., J. Mol. Spectry., 17, 276 (1965).

4. D. White, P. N. Walsh, L. L. Ames, and H. W. Goldstein, Thermodynamics of Nuclear Materials, International Atomic Energy Agency, Vienna (1962), p. 417.

5. MgO: L. Brewer, S. Trajmar, and R. Berg, Astrophys. J., 135, 955 (1962); L. Brewer and S. Trajmar, J. Chem. Phys., 36, 1585 (1962); S. Trajmar and G. E. Ewing, Astrophys. J., 142, 77 (1965). SrO: M. Kaufman, L. Wharton, and W. Klemperer, J. Chem. Phys., 43, 943 (1965). BaO: R. Brooks and M. Kaufman, J. Chem. Phys., 43, 3406 (1965).

6. L. Brewer, Proc. Robert A. Welch Foundation Conf. Chem. Res., 6, 47 (1963).

7. T. Tsuji, Proc. Japan Acad., 40, 99 (1964); H. C. Lord, Icarus, 4, 279 (1965).

8. W. Weltner, Jr., and D. McLeod, Jr., J. Mol. Spectry., 17, 276 (1965).

9. L. Gausset, G. Herzberg, A. Lagerqvist, and B. Rosen, Astrophys. J., 142, 45 (1965).

10. W. Weltner, Jr., and D. McLeod, Jr., J. Chem. Phys., 40, 1305 (1964).

11. K. S. Pitzer and E. Clementi, J. Am. Chem. Soc., 81, 4477 (1959); S. J. Strickler and K. S. Pitzer, in Molecular Orbitals in Chemistry, Physics and Biology, P. Lowdin and P. Pullman, eds., Academic, New York (1964), p. 281.

12. W. Weltner, Jr., and D. McLeod, Jr., J. Chem. Phys., 41, 235 (1964).

13. M. Cowperthwaite and S. H. Bauer, J. Chem. Phys., 36, 1743 (1962); R. E. Duff and S. H. Bauer, J. Chem. Phys., 36, 1754 (1962).

14. M. N. Plooster and T. B. Reed, J. Chem. Phys., 31, 66 (1959); R. F. Baddour and J. M. Iwasyk, Ind. Eng. Chem., 1, 169 (1962).

15. A. J. Merer and D. N. Travis, Can. J. Phys., 43, 1795 (1965).

16. R. W. Nicholls, W. H. Parkinson, and E. M. Reeves, Appl. Opt., 2, 919 (1963).

17. P. H. Kasai and W. Weltner, Jr., J. Chem. Phys., 43, 2553 (1965).

18. P. H. Kasai and W. Weltner, Jr., to be published.

19. C. K. Jen, S. N. Foner, E. L. Cochran, and V. A. Bowers, Phys. Rev., 112, 1169 (1958).

Selected Problem Areas in High-Temperature Chemistry

S. S. PENNER

Department of the Aerospace and Mechanical Engineering Sciences
University of California, San Diego
La Jolla, California

In this note, we shall confine our attention to brief remarks of basic problem areas in high-temperature chemistry that are perhaps best identified with the interface between gas dynamics and chemical reaction processes. These coupled problems are generally encountered in such diverse problem areas as combustion and propulsion engines, planetary entry phenomena, gas-dynamic techniques adapted to the chemical process industries, and the design and manufacture of chemical propellants.

CHEMICAL KINETICS

Among the many elementary chemical rate processes that have been inadequately studied are such relatively simple reactions as

$$O_2^- + O \rightarrow O_2 + O^- ,$$
$$O_2^- + O_3 \rightarrow O_2 + O_3^- ;$$
$$e + O_3 \rightarrow O^- + O_2 ;$$

and dissociative attachment involving O_2. Reaction rates for the direct recombination of negative and positive ions have never been measured quantitatively. Oxidative processes of polymeric materials have been studied, to some extent, especially by the use of shock-tube techniques, but are clearly not sufficiently well understood to permit useful theoretical predictions of ablation phenomena in high-speed flows. Although limited success has been achieved in the theoretical prediction of such elementary processes as the dissociation mechanism of diatomic molecules, the challenging experimental verification remains to be performed.

OPACITIES OF HEATED GASES

Quantitative spectroscopic measurements of heated gases, as well as the corresponding theoretical studies on opacities, remain difficult experimental and analytical problems in spite of the successful implementation of such diverse experimental tools as shock tubes, ballistic ranges, and stable electric arcs. This type of information is of inestimable value, for example, in diagnostic work on reacting mixtures and on wakes behind hypersonic re-entry vehicles. It also enters into a wide variety of applications, including radiant-heat transfer processes, which become of dominant importance as the flight speeds or reactor temperatures are progressively raised.

GAS-DYNAMIC TECHNIQUES FOR THE PRODUCTION OF CHEMICAL COMPOUNDS

The full potential of coupled gas-dynamic processes and chemical changes for the production of chemical compounds has yet to be exploited. Shock tubes and de Laval nozzles are by now well-identified tools for the study of reaction rates in flow systems. A successful gas-dynamic procedure for the measurement of heats of adsorption has been devised.

There are numerous examples of recommendations to adapt these techniques for the use of chemical production processes. The rapidly repeating shock tube has become a "comprex engine" for chemical manufacture but has yet to be developed to the point where it is an economical alternative to other procedures. "Freezing" of chemical intermediates during expansion through a de Laval nozzle is a well-recognized occurrence in rockets and ramjets but has not yet been adapted to desirable applications. Some progress has been achieved in defining the mechanism of reactions in turbulent media but, to this date, the new knowledge has not been put to good use in process industries utilizing turbulent flow. Perhaps the most direct indications of useful adaptation of new knowledge in high-temperature kinetics may be found in recent developments of arc techniques for chemical manufacture.

The author is inclined to the view that full exploitation of new knowledge on the coupling between reactions and gas flows will have far-reaching effects on the chemical production industries.

HIGH-ENERGY PROPELLANTS

A program for the design of new high-energy propellants, which was sponsored by the Advanced Research Projects Agency of the Department of Defense in several chemical and rocket laboratories, has stimulated a wide variety of new synthetic processes although no superpropellant was developed. Concurrently, a basic program was brought into being on bond-energy and heat of combustion studies of interesting new compounds. The benefit to the chemical process industries of this type of activity is difficult to estimate. However, it is apparent that the termination of DOD support will leave a serious void that can only be filled by new programs of sufficient scope and demand to assure continuation of relatively uncommitted research with truly unlimited goals. Perhaps the continuing, though relatively small, programs on free-radical stabilization, large-scale manufacture of excited atoms and molecules, and other wondrous objectives will provide the impetus for continued discovery in fields that lack the fascination of particle physics or of biochemical research on the origin of life.

Re-entry Ablation and Wake Chemistry
of Polymers, Composites, and Refractory Materials

JOHN I. SLAUGHTER
Aerospace Corporation
El Segundo, California

The thermal protection of critical components of rocket engines and re-entry heat shields is accomplished by the sacrificial combustion or sublimation of a portion of the exposed component. If one compares the re-entry and rocket-engine thermal environments with existing high-temperature laboratory facilities, he quickly realizes the inadequacies of ground test facilities and diagnostic tools in relation to operating temperatures, reaction rates, pressures, and high-temperature processes for which data are needed.

The behavior of materials exposed to severe thermal environments is dominated by kinetic and mass-transport effects, and a complete phenomenological understanding of the chemistry of re-entry, for example, requires the combined efforts of an interdisciplinary team consisting of scientists trained in high-temperature materials, computer technology, spectroscopy, plasma physics, reaction kinetics, gas dynamics, and electromagnetics. The calculation of the re-entry radar wake is a typical problem that can be handled through an interdisciplinary approach. Communication problems among individuals and among technology groups arise in evaluating existing data and in achieving further advances in high-temperature chemistry.

A comprehensive review of the gas-phase chemistry of re-entry reveals serious deficiencies in the current supply of data from the point of view of the systems engineer responsible for designing and analyzing the performance of materials and structures subjected to temperatures of $4{,}000\,^\circ K$ and above.

The rate of electron production in high-temperature air and in air with ablation products is important in nonequilibrium boundary-layer and wake chemistry. A review of the chemi-ionization reactions of air and of nitrogen, and the combustion reactions of hydrocarbons, fluorocarbons, and carbon vapor indicates that an understanding of gas-phase kinetics and electron production at extremely high temperatures will require additional knowledge of the reactions of atoms, molecules, and radicals in excited states.

Deionization, recombination, and electron-attachment reactions are equally important in understanding wake chemistry. The kinetics of alkali metal deionization, electron capture by cooling, and electron attachment by solid and homogeneous recombination reactions are of great significance. Studies of high-temperature electron-attachment rates can provide data on wake chemistry as well as basic data on electronic energy levels in negative ions. Such information is especially needed for diatomic species, radicals, and atoms.

Diagnostic flight instrumentation is needed for characterizing the high-temperature flow fields and measuring wake temperatures, for the identification of species in excited states, and for the determination of electron concentrations.

Relatively few materials will be able to satisfy future high-temperature requirements. The aerothermochemistry of graphite, hafnium carbide, and tungsten in relation to some typical re-entry environments can be used to illustrate typical problems encountered in utilizing existing data for high-temperature performance analyses. Many of the existing data on heterogeneous reaction rates are conflicting and are not as basic as one would desire. Too often, such "basic" data include overriding mass transportation phenomena which are not included in the analyses. Moreover, much of the current supply of data is limited to temperatures below the range $1,000$-$1,700\,^{\circ}C$ and requires too large an extrapolation for reliable use at temperatures above $3,000\,^{\circ}C$.

Much of the available mass-spectroscopic thermodynamic data in the literature is unreliable, and the general usefulness of such data is restricted. An urgent need exists for additional identifications of high-temperature and high-pressure species for Langmuir evaporations, especially for metal - metal oxide systems. Such data are required before new ideas can occur and further advances can be made in the protection of refractory metals at high temperatures. Cation - anion diffusion studies and emittance measurements are needed for pure metals, ternary systems of oxides, oxidized tungsten, carbides, and other materials.

Air - plasma arc tests of refractory materials offer an opportunity for interpreting the behavior of materials on the basis of available data and theory, and thus for the revelation of gross inconsistancies, omitted species, and anomalous chemical behavior.

Studies of Condensed-Phase Microspecimens at High Temperatures Obtained with Intense Thermal Pulses

L. S. NELSON
Sandia Laboratory
Albuquerque, New Mexico

INTRODUCTION

Recently, more and more high-temperature experiments have been carried out by suddenly heating condensed-phase microspecimens with intense thermal pulses. It will be shown here that this method offers scientists new freedoms to explore temperature ranges and chemical systems hitherto prohibitive in conventional high-temperature technology. Examples from the literature will be discussed first to illustrate the variety of experiments that are possible. Then our current studies of burning droplets of zirconium will be summarized, to show the specific and sometimes quite precise information that may be obtained from a favorable high-temperature system.

A typical microspecimen is a solid or liquid body with a characteristic dimension, D, in the submillimeter to micron range. The simplest shapes are spheres, cylinders, and sheets, where the characteristic dimensions are their diameters or thicknesses. Thus, powders, small spheroids, tiny droplets, fine wires, fibers, thin foils, and films would be considered microspecimens or aggregates thereof.

Microspecimens are particularly well suited for chemical studies at high temperatures because of their high area-to-mass ratio, which is proportional to $1/D$ for the simple geometries of spheres, cylinders, and plates. When a microspecimen is exposed to a given flow of energy, its temperature rise, ΔT, will depend to good approximation directly upon this ratio; that is, $\Delta T = K/D$, where K is a constant characteristic of the energy flow, and of the shape, state, and properties of the microspecimen. Thus, as D becomes small, the temperature rise may become very large, sometimes several thousand degrees Kelvin.

33

The high area-to-mass ratios also favor rapid heating and quenching and high reaction rates with external reagents. Consequently, it is often possible to start at room temperature, perform a high-temperature experiment, and return to room temperature all within a small fraction of a second.

The basic advantages of using microspecimens at high temperatures are the avoidance of supports or containers and the ability to confine the entire experimental region within a cold-wall system. Conventional high-temperature studies are seriously limited by the high reactivity or structural failure above about $2,500\,^{\circ}K$ of the refractory solids normally used for crucibles, supports, furnaces, liners, and heating elements.

With microspecimens, however, it is usually possible to make sheets or cylinders self-supporting, at least for the short duration of the experiments, by clamping at the extremities. Spheres normally are studied in free fall, taking advantage of their brief reaction times to eliminate the need for excessive apparatus heights. Sometimes, the microspecimens may be supported temporarily on nonrefractory materials which essentially disappear during heating, hardly perturbing the measurements of interest. Levitation may be possible in some cases.

Modern measuring techniques provide both the sensitivity and resolution to obtain meaningful data; modern manipulative techniques enable the delicate specimens to be prepared, positioned, and examined easily.

EXPERIMENTAL

The microspecimens used in this work may be prepared in many ways, among which are rolling, drawing, beating, grinding, extruding, spraying, spheroidizing, microtoming, cleaving, vapor depositing, sputtering, and chemical etching. Normally there is at least one technique usable for each substance, although it is sometimes difficult to perform the size reduction without serious contamination.

Heating is performed with a number of rapid energy-transfer devices including shock waves; various radiation sources such as image furnaces, flash lamps, lasers, and plasma torches; capacitor discharges through electrical conductors; and chemical heating with flames, pyrotechnics, and explosions.

Measurements on the microspecimens may be performed with still and high-speed photography, emission and absorption spectroscopy, high-speed photographic and photoelectric pyrometry, fast thermocouples, and other devices that produce electrical parameters for oscilloscope display. Sometimes, the reactions may be interrupted at various stages by quenching the microspecimen in liquefied rare gases, followed by conventional analytical procedures, or the microspecimens may be allowed to react completely before examination. Usually, several of these methods are used simultaneously.

High-temperature studies of microspecimens are performed with the condensed material suspended in a matrix of some sort. The condensed phases may be solid or liquid, while the matrices may be a vacuum or low- or high-pressure gases, liquids, or solids. The processes of interest normally involve either changes of phase or chemical reactions.

RESULTS

Some typical studies of microspecimens with intense thermal pulses have been summarized in Table 1. The temperatures achieved by the various techniques range from nearly $7,000\,^\circ$K to as low as $1,000\,^\circ$K. However, the upper limit of temperature will probably be governed more by the chemical and physical characteristics of the system than by the experimental procedure used.

Combustion of Zirconium Droplets

In this section, our work on the combustion of freely falling zirconium droplets will be described briefly in order to demonstrate specifically the important information that can be obtained by pulse-heating of condensed-phase microspecimens. Since zirconium with moderately high specific area reportedly burns in oxygen at temperatures near $3,500\,^\circ$K (13), this example illustrates a high-temperature process that probably could not be handled by conventional furnace techniques, yet is easily studied by the use of microspecimens.

Droplets with diameters between 50 and 500 μm have been formed from small squares of zirconium foil in the flash heating apparatus (12) shown in Figure 1. Single squares are dropped from the top of the tube and are melted by an intense light pulse ($\sim$20 thermal J/cm^2 flash) as they fall through the portion of the glass chamber surrounded by the helical flash lamp. If sufficient oxygen is present, the newly formed droplets ignite and burn luminously as they fall. The behavior of the glowing droplets may be recorded photographically, or the droplets may be quenched by inserting a vessel of liquid argon at various heights in the chamber. The quenched droplets subsequently may be examined by conventional analytical procedures.

TABLE 1. Typical Studies of Microspecimens Heated with Intense Thermal Pulses

Process	Sample	$D(\mu m)$	Surroundings	Heat Source	Measurements	Results	Ref.
α-β phase change in titanium	Strip	375	Vacuum	Capacitor discharge through sample	Resistance of sample; thermocouple voltage	Obtained C_p vs T (25-800 °C); $\Delta H_{\alpha-\beta} = 800 \pm 48$ cal/mole	1
Vaporization of refractory solids	Various powdered elements and inorganic oxides, hydrides, carbides, sulfides, etc.	50-100	Driving gases: H_2 or He. Reactant gases: H_2, N_2, O_2	Shock tube	Time-resolved emission and absorption spectra; shock parameters	Spectra of atoms, gaseous oxides; TiN; oscillator strengths; temperatures near 5,000 °K; autoionization	2-5
Gases in metal films	Thin metal films on glass or Pt foil	<2	He, vacuum	Flash lamp	Gas chromatography	Analyses of H, Ar, O, N, CH_4, CO and CO_2 in Ta films	6
Decomposition of $KMnO_4$	Crystals of $KMnO_4$ (~100μg)	–	Vacuum	Flash lamp	Mass spectra; time-resolved spectra; conventional analyses	Separate thermal and photoreactions; observe gaseous O_2, Mn, K, MnO, MnO_3	7
Vaporization of tungsten	Wire, strip	13-14	Ar, He, N_2	Flash lamp	Time-resolved absorption spectra	Tungsten vapor at ~7000 °K	8
Combustion of zirconium droplets	Spherical drops in free fall	50-500	O_2, N_2, Ar and their mixtures	Flash lamp	Photography, spectroscopy, pyrometry, deflections from plates, analyses of quenched droplets	Oxynitride formation; explosions of droplets; supercooling; reaction rates	9-12 17

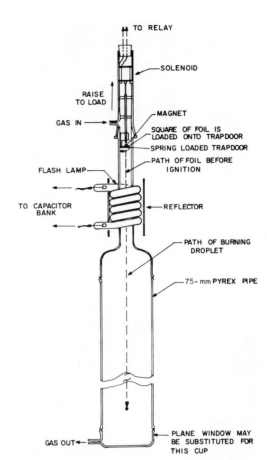

Figure 1. Flash heating apparatus used for forming and igniting metal droplets.

Combustions with Explosions   When submillimeter zirconium droplets burn under ordinary circumstances, the combustions almost always terminate in an abrupt explosion or fragmentation a few tenths of a second after ignition (9,12). A typical explosion is shown in the time-exposed photograph in Figure 2. The traces often show fragments hurled a meter or so from the center of the explosion.

In order to determine the cause of these curious explosions, droplets quenched in liquid argon at various stages of combustion before the explosions were examined by x-ray diffraction. When the droplets had burned in pure oxygen or oxygen - argon mixtures, the patterns of zirconium and zirconium dioxide were observed. However, when the droplets had burned in air or other oxygen - nitrogen mixtures, not only were patterns of unreacted zirconium and zirconium dioxide observed as before, but, in addition, intense patterns due to zirconium nitride and weaker patterns due to several zirconium oxynitrides (14) were also observed. Sometimes when metal and gases of ordinary purity were used, the droplets that had burned in oxygen -

37

Figure 2. Typical explosion of zirconium droplet burning in air at 125 torr. Droplet diameter initially was 270 μm.

argon mixtures also showed faint patterns due to zirconium nitride, presumably due to nitrogen impurities. From the x-ray evidence, it became apparent that nitrogen was participating actively in the combustion of liquid zirconium.

It was then surmised that the explosions are not really characteristic of the high-temperature combination of zirconium with oxygen, but instead are actually caused by the presence of nitrogen in the combustion system. The experiments shown in Figure 3 were performed to test these hypotheses (10). At the left, a 525-μm droplet of

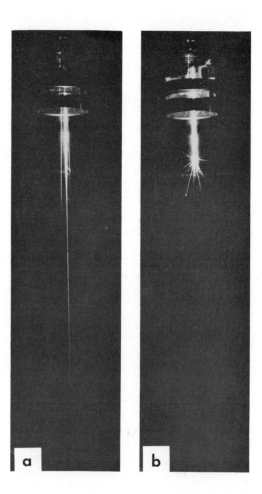

Figure 3. The combustion of a freely falling zirconium droplet in oxygen (left) and in a mixture of 4.5 percent nitrogen and 95.5 percent oxygen (right). In each case, the droplets are burning in a 75-mm Pyrex tube containing the oxidizing gas at 625 torr flowing downward at 5.0 liters/min. Droplet diameter is 525 μm. The weak traces are reflections from the walls of the chamber.

zirconium was burned in pure oxygen at 625 torr. Notice the long unbranched trace which gradually extinguished. At the right, a droplet was burned under identical conditions, except that 4.5 percent of gaseous nitrogen had been added to the oxygen. Here the droplet fell for a short time and then exploded violently. When the zirconium was alloyed with 4 atom percent of nitrogen before ignition, and the combustion was performed in pure oxygen, photographs were obtained similar to the one in Figure 3b.

It was thus shown (10) that the explosions of burning zirconium droplets could be caused by adding small amounts of nitrogen either to the gaseous oxidizer or to the metal prior to ignition. Further studies have shown that as the diameters of the droplets decrease, progressively smaller amounts of nitrogen are required to cause the explosions. Thus, even normal nitrogen impurities may be sufficient to cause the explosion of small zirconium droplets.

The action of the nitrogen during combustion is thought to be as follows:

$$Zr \xrightarrow[\substack{O_2 \\ \\ ZrN_y}]{O_2, N_2} ZrO_xN_y \xrightarrow{O_2} ZrO_2 + N_2 \uparrow$$

Here, zirconium burns in oxygen that contains nitrogen (upper arrow) to give an intermediate oxynitride, designated ZrO_xN_y. The same oxynitride alternatively may be obtained by burning zirconium that contains alloyed nitrogen, designated ZrN_y, in pure oxygen (lower arrow). Now, as the oxynitride, ZrO_xN_y, takes up more oxygen, the composition of the burning droplet approaches that of the thermodynamically favored end product, zirconium dioxide, with release of nitrogen. At some stage of the combustion, the solubility of nitrogen in the melt will be exceeded, and the gas will be released, causing the fragmentation. Supersaturation may be involved here.

Explosion-Free Combustions In the trace shown in Figure 3a, it can be seen that a large portion of the observable combustion of the zirconium droplet has been obscured by the explosion. By reducing the concentration of nitrogen or other gas-related impurities sufficiently, it is possible to eliminate the explosions and thereby explore a previously unknown region of the burning process—that which takes place after the explosions would have occurred in the usual nitrogen-containing combustion situation.

This new part of the combustion was examined by direct microweighing of 525-μm droplets of zirconium quenched in liquid argon after burning for various times in pure oxygen at 625 torr. The

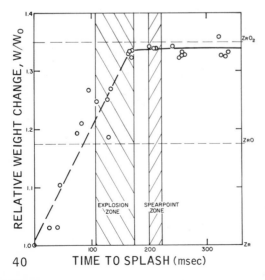

Figure 4. Relative weight change of 525-μm droplets of zirconium burning in oxygen at 625 torr, as a function of time to strike surface of liquid argon (combustion time). Explosion zone indicates time span during which droplets would have exploded if 4.5 percent of gaseous nitrogen had been added to the oxygen. In the absence of nitrogen, droplets suddenly brightened within time span designated as spearpoint zone. Average composition of droplet is indicated at right.

results of these gravimetric studies are shown in Figure 4. Also indicated is the explosion zone, which denotes the range of times at which these same droplets would explode if 4.5 percent of nitrogen were added to the gaseous oxygen (corresponding to the right side of Figure 3).

In Figure 4, the droplets increase in weight with time until (in the absence of explosion) the composition reaches ZrO_{2-x}, where $x \sim 0.04$. At this point, the oxidation rate decreases, with a slower approach to the stoichiometric composition, ZrO_2, thereafter.

Two phenomena that can be observed at times beyond the explosion time will be discussed here. These are spearpoints and oxidation rates.

Spearpoints have been observed for many years in time-exposed photographs of sparks formed when metals are abrasively ground (15). These spear-like images are seen as traces of individual burning droplets which steadily decrease in brightness, abruptly increase, and then gradually diminish until extinguishment. Spearpoints are readily observed in the explosion-free combustion of zirconium droplets [see traces in Figures 3(a) and 5(a)].

The nature of the spearpoints was investigated by inserting an inclined Pyrex plate at various heights in the path of the droplets' fall (11). This is shown in Figures 5(b) and (c). When the plate was placed above the shoulder of the spearpoint (above the sudden intensification) the droplets adhered to the plate, sometimes with signs of splattering as they landed [Figure 5(b)]. Under the microscope, the droplets were seen to be flattened shapes which apparently had been liquid at the time of collision. When the plate was placed below the shoulder of the spearpoint, however, the glowing droplets did not adhere. Instead, they bounced elastically from the plate and subsequently from the glass walls of the combustion chamber [Figure 5(c)]. Dense spheres of white oxide were retrieved from the bottom of the chamber afterward.

On the basis of these experiments, the shoulder of the spearpoint has been ascribed to the solidification of the burning droplet (11). This is consistent with the stage of combustion at which the spearpoints occur, which has been designated in Figure 4 as the spearpoint zone. Note that the spearpoints occur shortly after the rapid weight gain to ZrO_{2-x} ceases; that is, just after the fuel (zirconium) is essentially exhausted. The temperature at which the solidification occurs is probably very close to the melting point of ZrO_2, which is near $3,100°K$.

The magnitude of the intensity increase was puzzling at first. Photoelectric densitometry of spearpoints recorded on calibrated emulsions showed that the intensity of light emitted ($\lambda > 6,200$ Å) by the droplet just after solidification was 3.93 times greater than that emitted just before solidifcation.

It was first suggested (11) that the increase in intensity was due

41

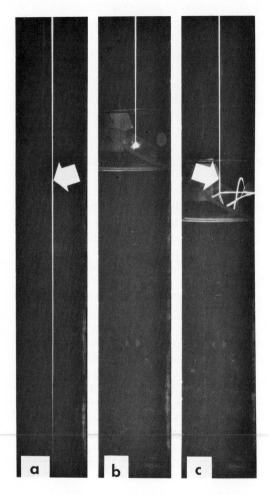

Figure 5. Time exposures of freely falling zirconium droplets burning in flowing oxygen at 625 torr, photographed by their own incandescence. Shoulders of spearpoints are indicated by arrows. Droplet diameter was 525 μm. Width of each photograph corresponds to approximately 7 cm. In (a), the droplet falls freely, showing complete spearpoint. In (b) and (c), glass plate has been inserted in droplet's path of fall above and below shoulder of spearpoint, respectively. Adherence to plate in (b) indicates molten droplet; elastic deflection in (c) indicates solidified droplet.

to a large increase in the emittance of the droplet as it solidified. This view was supported by a difference in room-temperature color of droplets quenched just above and just below the spearpoint. However, recent high-temperature measurements indicate only a small difference between the emittances of liquid and solid zirconia (16)— nowhere near the almost fourfold increase required for an explanation based solely on an emittance change.

Another explanation has recently been proposed (17), based on supercooling. Here the decrease in intensity is caused by a supercooling of the molten oxide droplet below its equilibrium melting temperature. The abrupt brightening is caused by nucleation and rapid crystallization with a corresponding increase in thermal emission as the droplet's temperature rises again to the freezing point.

A supercooling of approximately $500°$ below the freezing point near $3,100°K$ is required to achieve the fourfold increase in emission.

The supercooling explanation is supported by experiments in which the burning droplets were deflected from a steeply inclined aluminum plate (17). It was possible to suppress the formation of spearpoints with high probability when the glancing collisions occurred between 152 and 200 msec (for $525-\mu m$ droplets of zirconium burning in O_2 at 625 torr), presumably because vibrational nucleation prevented supercooling of the droplets. Since this span of time immediately precedes the solidification of the droplets (the spearpoint zone in Figure 4), it is presumed to be approximately the duration of supercooling.

Phenomena analogous to spearpointing have been observed when supercooled droplets of metals suddenly freeze (18). This is known as recalescence or the "blick" effect. The degree of supercooling commonly observed in metals is $\sim 0.18\ T_{melting}$ (in $°K$) (18). If the degree of supercooling observed in burning zirconium droplets is actually $500°$, then the degree of supercooling here is $\sim 0.16\ T_{melting}$.

The kinetics of oxidation of molten metals can be studied with weight-gain data of the type shown in Figure 4. In a preliminary way, we have placed a least-squares straight line through the relative weights in the region of rapid increase. This gives an averaged reaction rate of 113 mg of O_2/cm^2-sec for $525-\mu m$ droplets of zirconium burning in free fall in oxygen at 625 torr. Analogous measurements on $270-\mu m$ droplets of zirconium burning in a mixture of 20 percent oxygen in argon at 625 torr indicate an oxidation rate of 11.5 mg of O_2/cm^2-sec. For $270-\mu m$ droplets burning in air at 625 torr, the droplets increased weight at a rate of 16.5 mg/cm^2-sec, but as shown above, this is a combined rate of oxidation and nitridation.

CONCLUSIONS

It is hoped that the value of studying microspecimens at high temperatures with intense thermal pulses has been demonstrated here. Valuable information certainly can be obtained this way. In my opinion, ingenious application of techniques such as those outlined here offers the greatest hope for studying condensed phases at temperatures above $3,000°K$.

This work was supported by the United States Atomic Energy Commission.

REFERENCES

1. R. Parker, Trans. Met. Soc. AIME, 233, 1545 (1965).
2. R. W. Nicholls, W. H. Parkinson, and E. M. Reeves, Appl. Opt., 2, 919 (1963).
3. W. H. Parkinson and E. M. Reeves, Proc. Roy. Soc. (London), A282, 265 (1964).
4. W. H. Parkinson and E. M. Reeves, Can. J. Phys., 41, 702 (1963).
5. W. R. S. Garton, W. H. Parkinson, and E. M. Reeves, Astrophys. J., 140, 1269 (1964).
6. W. G. Guldner, Anal. Chem., 35, 1744 (1963); also private communication.
7. J. G. Kay, Department of Chemistry, University of Illinois, private communication.
8. L. S. Nelson and N. A. Kuebler, J. Chem. Phys., 39, 1055 (1963).
9. L. S. Nelson and N. L. Richardson, J. Phys. Chem., 68, 1268 (1964).
10. L. S. Nelson, Science, 148, 1594 (1965).
11. L. S. Nelson, Nature, 207, 741 (1965).
12. L. S. Nelson, Pyrodynamics, 3, 121 (1965).
13. P. D. Harrison and A. D. Yoffe, Proc. Roy. Soc. (London), A261, 357 (1961).
14. J. C. Gilles, Bull. Soc. Chim. France, 2118 (1962).
15. W. Baukloh, Arch. Eisenhuettenw., 13, 543 (1940).
16. L. Eisner, D. W. Fisher, and R. F. Leftwich, in Thermal Techniques, P. Glaser and R. F. Walker, eds., Plenum, New York (1964), pp. 113–129.
17. L. S. Nelson, Nature, in press.
18. D. Turnbull and R. E. Cech, J. Appl. Phys., 21, 804 (1950).
19. F. E. Littman, A. E. Levy-Pascal, and N. A. Tiner, Progr. Astronautics Aeronautics, 15, 279 (1964).
20. E. M. Mouradian and L. Baker, Jr., Nucl. Sci. Eng., 15, 388 (1963).

QUESTIONS ADDRESSED TO DR. NELSON

QUESTION BY JOHN L. MARGRAVE: How well do the oxidation rates from your technique compare with static-oxidation-rate studies of $Zr + O_2$?

ANSWER: Published values for rates of oxidation above the melting point of zirconium are scarce. Harrison and Yoffe (13) report 14.6 mg of O_2/cm^2-sec for 250-μm zirconium wire burning in a mixture of 45 percent oxygen in nitrogen and 65 mg of O_2/cm^2-sec for 600-μm zirconium wire burning in a mixture of 20 percent nitrogen in oxygen. Littman, et al. (19) report an average weight increase of the order of 1.5 mg/cm^2-sec when 2-10 mm molten droplets of an alloy of 10 percent U in Zr were oxidized in air while levitated in an induction heater. Since the gas compositions, area-to-mass ratios, and probably the burning temperatures differ from ours, direct comparison of results is difficult. There seems to be at least order of magnitude agreement, however.

Our measurement of 11.5 mg of O_2/cm^2-sec in 20 percent oxygen in argon at 625 torr agrees fairly well with calculations of Mouradian and Baker (20) for zirconium burning in flowing air at 760 torr. The comparison should be good, because they assume nitrogen to be inert. By interpolating their values, a rate of 16 mg of O_2/cm^2-sec was obtained for 270-μm droplets falling at 150 cm/sec. If this value can be decreased by the ratio of total gas pressures, 625/760, the calculated rate becomes 13 mg of O_2/cm^2-sec.

QUESTION BY R. B. BADACHHAPE: Is there any correlation between the change in the intensity of radiation from the molten drop and its composition?

ANSWER: Both the intensity and spectral distribution of the light emitted by the burning zirconium droplets change as the combustions proceed. Continua are observed throughout the reactions. In some cases, however, additional banded emissions from ZrO are recorded early in the burning, but disappear gradually with time. In general, the light emitted is sensitive to droplet diameter and the pressure and composition of the gaseous phase. It would be premature at our current level of understanding to try to relate emitted intensities to droplet composition.

QUESTION BY R. B. BADACHHAPE: Can one determine the composition of the drop knowing its temperature (as intensity is related to temperature)?

ANSWER: Again, the complex interplay of droplet diameter and pressure and composition of the gaseous phase with the nature of the emitted light (our only means of determining temperature at present) would make the determination of composition by the temperature of the droplet difficult. Perhaps the end of the reaction could be related to a rapid decrease in intensity, but otherwise, the analysis of droplets quenched in liquid argon seems to be a more valuable approach.

QUESTION BY LEO BREWER: TaO is a very stable gaseous molecule. How does Guldner get O away from vaporized TaO?

ANSWER: The analysis of small amounts of oxygen in thin tantalum films has been most successful when the films were supported on thin platinum foils. When the tantalum - platinum combinations are exposed to radiation from the flash lamp, Guldner detects molecular oxygen with the gas chromotograph. Rather than directly forming gaseous tantalum and TaO, it is possible that as the metals are heated, they first form a very dilute alloy of tantalum in platinum in which the solubility of oxygen may be quite low. As this vaporizes, oxygen may be released before the gaseous TaO molecule has a chance to form.

Some Present and Future Problems of High-Temperature Chemistry

HAROLD L. SCHICK
Lockheed Missiles and Space Company
Palo Alto, California

INTRODUCTION

To attempt to name all the important problems of the field of high-temperature chemistry, even the present ones, would be a large and difficult task. To extrapolate toward the next one or two decades and to name the high-temperature areas that will be or should be emphasized would be even more difficult. Present estimates, therefore, can expect only to be crude and incomplete. These estimates must be made by extrapolating from the present, keeping in mind the expected shifts in interest occasioned by a variety of factors, including technological advances; the effects of additional space, oceanic, and deep mining exploration; the effects of possible hot and cold wars; the effects of a population explosion; the effects of the growing influence of the less-developed nations; and the effects of other factors, some of which may yet be undefined.

Let us first very briefly review the present status of high-temperature chemistry.

SOME CURRENT AREAS OF INTEREST OF HIGH-TEMPERATURE CHEMISTRY

Interest in various practical applications of high-temperature chemistry has been spurred, including heat shields for re-entry vehicles, materials subject to the nuclear fireball environment, rocket-propulsion devices, energy conversion devices, electronics, and industrial applications such as chemical syntheses, metallurgical processes, and ceramic technology. Chemists who have dealt with these problems have been theoreticians or experimenters; they have dealt with such fundamental and basic tools as chemical thermodynamics, chemical kinetics, and spectroscopy, and some have used purely empirical techniques to achieve their objectives.

High-temperature data that have been and are being obtained include thermodynamic properties of condensed or gaseous phases; chemical kinetic rate constants in gas phase, in condensed phases, or in heterogeneous systems; transport properties in gases and in condensed phases; and phase-diagram data for binary and more complicated systems.

Of these, a type of data that has rightly received much consideration has been that of chemical thermodynamics. Such data can be used in most, if not all, of the applied high-temperature problems. The importance of such efforts has been emphasized by the development of the JANAF Thermochemical Tables and by the creation of the National Standard Reference Data System administrated by the National Bureau of Standards. Clearly, such efforts should be continued.

SOME FUTURE PROBLEMS OF HIGH-TEMPERATURE CHEMISTRY

It would appear that current problems will continue to face the high-temperature chemist. In general, it would appear that there will also be more difficult applications (i.e., higher temperatures) than those now encountered. According to a recent report, NASA contemplates such future projects as additional flights in Pioneer series of solar probes, which will approach to within 0.1 astronomical unit of the sun, posing new heating problems [1]. Re-entry conditions on returning from Mars flights, at velocities of about 50,000 ft/sec, will cause much more severe heating problems than those now faced by the Apollo program. Another indication of the need for improvement of high-temperature processes was noted by the statement that one type of fuel cell was not favored for long life because it "utilizes a high-temperature process and implies materials problems." These examples illustrate two important areas in which the need for further knowledge will spur additional work: higher-temperature environments and reliability and longevity at high temperature.

SOME SUGGESTIONS FOR FUTURE EMPHASIS

Chemical Thermodynamics

In the field of thermodynamic compilations, there is a need for continued expanded projects of the JANAF type. These can be expanded to include more elements since the present JANAF effort has been confined primarily to the elements of low atomic weight of interest in rocket propulsion. Also, the JANAF compilation has been restricted to temperatures up to 6,000°K. With the increasing emphasis on projects involving even higher temperatures, it would appear advisable to consider compilations of thermodynamic data to much higher temperatures, perhaps 20,000°K or even higher, for many of the species and ions of interest.

Recently, JANAF has started publishing data for atomic ions. It is felt that this effort should be continued and expanded to include molecular ions as well.

Dr. Cubicciotti has pointed out our lack of knowledge of thermodynamic properties of condensed phases at high temperature; this writer agrees heartily with his recommendations. There is clearly a need for experimental and theoretical work to provide a better understanding of the variation of thermodynamic parameters for condensed phases at high temperature.

Chemical Kinetics

Our knowledge in this field is still extremely limited. Bauer (2) has reviewed chemical kinetics studies in shock tubes, and Benson and DeMore (3) have reviewed the over-all subject of gas kinetics. The latter have also suggested the need for an international journal of gas-phase kinetics.

For many of the old and new problems facing us, there will continue to be a need for information on experimental and theoretical kinetics. Knowledge of reaction rates in solid-phase media, in heterogeneous solid - gas reactions, and in homogeneous gas-phase reactions will be of interest in a variety of fields, including metallurgy and ablation. Activities involving theory of simple reactions, compilation activities, and experimental studies should be encouraged.

Transport Properties

For many of our current and future problems involving the study of ablation phenomena, boundary-layer theory, flames, and the effects of nuclear fireballs, there is a continued need for knowledge of transport and optical properties of gases at high temperatures. Such properties must be known more accurately in order to understand the behavior of these systems.

Information Processing and Education

In addition to the encouragement of continued research in thermodynamics, chemical kinetics, and related fields, it is believed essential that further advances in the high-temperature field could be spurred by additional changes in our information-processing and educational systems. It might be appropriate to have a journal (perhaps an international one) devoted to the subject of high temperatures. A precedent for such a journal was set by the Russians who started publishing High Temperature in 1963. This journal is translated into English by Consultants Bureau. At present, high-temperature data are scattered in numerous journals, such as the Journal of Chemical Physics, Journal of Physical Chemistry, Journal of the American Chemical Society, Combustion and Flame, Pyrodynamics, Journal of the American Ceramic Society, International Journal of Heat and Mass Transfer, Physics of Fluids, Journal of the Electrochemical Society, Fuel, Transactions of the Metallurgical Society of AIME, Journal of Molecular Spectroscopy, and Journal of the Less-Common Metals.

Another possibility that educators might consider is to give undergraduate and graduate courses and degrees in high-temperature chemistry. With increasing specialization in this country and abroad, it would appear that training designed especially for the high-temperature field would be extremely valuable.

REFERENCES

1. Anon., Missiles and Rockets, 17 (22), 103 (1965).
2. S. H. Bauer, Ann. Rev. Phys. Chem., 16, 245 (1965).
3. S. W. Benson and W. B. DeMore, Ann. Rev. Phys. Chem., 16, 397 (1965).

QUESTION ADDRESSED TO DR. SCHICK

QUESTION BY R. H. FOX: What is the state of our knowledge regarding transport of oxygen through oxide or other protective coatings on refractory substrates at temperatures above 2,000°K?

ANSWER: In recent years there has been a great deal of interest in, and work devoted to, the development of protective refractory coatings.

The following answer is only a very brief synopsis of some of the available information.

A recently translated book by Hauffe (1) discusses the role of structural defects in determining the rate of oxidation. Books dealing with the transport phenomena in solids include those of Barrer (2) and Crank (3). A review of diffusion data for metal systems in 1963 by Winslow (4) yielded 178 references. Other review articles include that of oxygen diffusion in oxides by Haul et al. (5) and in metals by Lazarus (6). VanThyne (7), Begley (8), Coombs (9), and Burte (10) have pointed out some of the current lines of research for refractory materials and for coatings. Materials that contain silicon or aluminum and that ultimately yield an SiO_2 or Al_2O_3 film are among the presently considered protective materials. The more refractive oxide materials such as ZrO_2, HfO_2, and ThO_2 are being investigated and ultimately may be utilized.

Actual experimental data for the diffusion of oxygen in refractory oxides is limited, especially for temperatures above 2,000°K. For Al_2O_3, data have been reported by Paladino and Coble (11,12) up to about 1,900° C (2173°K). Earlier information in this system was also published by Oishi and Kingery (13). In the case of SiO_2, Sucov (14) reported a diffusion coefficient given as $D = 1.51 \times 10^{-2} \exp (-71,200/RT)$ cm^2/sec. However, he concluded that current theories could not explain the pre-exponential factor. His data were for the range 925-1,225°C. Williams (15) reported a rather different value of diffusion constant than that of Sucov (14), finding that $D = 2 \times 10^{-9} \exp (-29,000/RT)$ cm^2/sec for the temperature range 850-1,250° C. Other data have been obtained by Haul and Dumbgen (15), Doremus (16), and Norton (17). In the case of the molybdenum silicides, which have been recently emphasized as coatings, there have been articles dealing with the structure of the oxide film by Bartlett et al. (19) and with its vaporization properties by Blair et al. (20).

For ZrO_2, data have been obtained by Debuigne and Lehr (21) and by Douglass (22). In the case of ThO_2, Edwards et al. (23) have measured the diffusion coefficient up to 1,500° C. Other systems for which diffusion data of oxygen through the refractory have been reported include the TiO_2 system by Bogomolov (24) and by Haul and Dumbgen (16); UO_2 by Auskern and Belle (25); and Cr_2O_3 by Hagel (26). In the case of HfO_2, there does not appear to be any readily available information regarding its ability to transport oxygen. However, there is ample interest in this material as a coating, as exemplified by the work of Mazdiyasni and Lynch (27) who have prepared and tested HfO_2 coatings on graphite substrates. Peters (28) has surveyed several refractory materials including MgO and HfO_2. VanThyne (7) has reported that hafnium containing 15-40 percent of tantalum is oxidation resistant to 4,000° F (2,480°K).

In conclusion, I would state that there is much work being done and much interest in the problem of protecting metals from oxygen attack at high temperature. However, it appears that the empirical approaches are more dominant. As yet, there do not appear to be many data dealing with transport phenomena in polycrystalline refractory materials at temperatures over 2,000° K. Even some of the available data for lower temperatures are controversial.

REFERENCES

1. K. Hauffe, Oxidation of Metals, Transl. of Oxydation von Metallen und Metallegierungen, Springer, Berlin (1956), Plenum, New York (1965).
2. R. M. Barrer, Diffusion in and Through Solids, Cambridge University Press, New York (1952).
3. J. Crank, Mathematics of Diffusion, Clarendon Press, Oxford (1956).
4. F. R. Winslow, J. Metals, 16, 589 (1964)
5. R. Haul, D. Just, and G. Dumbgen, "Oxygen Diffusion in Oxides," in Reactivity of Solids—Proceedings of 4th International Symposium, Amsterdam, 1960, J. H. DeBoer, W. G. Burgers, E. W. Gorter, J. P. F. Huesse, and G. C. A. Schmit, eds., Elsevier, Princeton, N.J. (1961), p.65.
6. D. Lazarus, "Diffusion in Metals," in Solid State Physics—Advances in Research and Applications, Vol. 10, F. Seitz and D. Turnbull, eds., Academic, New York (1960), p. 71.
7. R. VanThyne, "Exotic Materials," in Space/Aeronautics Research and Development Technical Handbook, 1964-1965, 42 (Sept. 1964), p. 163.
8. R. T. Begley, "Refractory Metals," in Space/Aeronautics Research and Development Technical Handbook, 1964-1965, 42 (Sept. 1964), p. 154.
9. L. C. Coombs, "Spacecraft and Missiles Structures," in Space/Aeronautics Research and Development Technical Handbook, 1965-1966, 44 (July 1965), p. 15.
10. H. M. Burte, Refractory Metals—An Assessment, AFSC, RTD ML-TR-64-344 (July 1964).
11. A. E. Paladino and R. L. Coble, J. Am. Ceramic Soc., 46, 133 (1963).
12. A. E. Paladino and R. L. Coble, J. Am. Ceramic Soc., 46, 460 (1963).
13. Y. H. Oishi and W. D. Kingery, J. Chem. Phys., 33, 480 (1960).
14. E. W. Sucov, J. Am. Ceramic Soc., 46, 14 (1963).
15. E. L. Williams, J. Am. Ceramic Soc., 48, 190 (1965).
16. R. Haul and G. Dumbgen, Z. Elektrochem., 66, 636 (1962).
17. R. H. Doremus, "Diffusion in Noncrystalline Silicates," in Modern Aspects of the Vitreous State, Vol. 2, J. D. Mackenzie, ed., Butterworth, Washington, D.C. (1962).
18. F. J. Norton, Nature, 191, 701 (1961).
19. R. W. Bartlett, J. W. McCamont, and P. R. Gage, J. Am. Ceramic Soc., 48, 551 (1965).
20. G. R. Blair, H. Levin, and R. O'Brien, J. Am. Ceramic Soc., 48, 430 (1965).
21. J. Debuigne and P. Lehr, Compt. Rend., 256, 1113 (1963); also Mem. Sci. Rev. Met., 60, 911 (1963); Chem. Abstr., 58, 9930d (1963); Chem. Abstr., 60, 10341g (1964) (Data for 600-850°C).
22. D. L. Douglass, USAEC-Euratom Joint Board Report, No. EURAEC-455 (1963).

23. H. S. Edwards, A. F. Rosenberg, and J. T. Bittell, USAEC Rept. No. ASD-TDR-63-635 (1963) (Data at 800-1,500°C for O_2 in ThO_2); Chem. Abstr., 7774d (1964).

24. V. N. Bogomolov, Soviet Phys.—Solid State, 5, 1468 (1964) (D = 1 × 10^{-5} cm^2/sec at 520°C for O_2).

25. A. B. Auskern and J. Belle, J. Nucl. Materials, 3, 267 (1961).

26. W. C. Hazel, J. Am. Ceramic Soc., 48, 70 (1965).

27. K. S. Mazdiyasni and C. T. Lynch, Synthesis and Pyrolysis of Metal Alkoxides as Potential Refractory Oxide Coatings for Graphite, USAEC Rept. ASD-TDR-63-322 (1963).

28. D. L. Peters, Chemical Corrosion of Rocket Liner Materials and Propellant Performance Studies, AD 425888 (1963).

Problem Areas in High-Temperature Chemistry

DANIEL CUBICCIOTTI
Stanford Research Institute
Menlo Park, California

This discussion concerns some areas that this writer feels should receive more attention in order to promote the understanding required to solve future problems in high-temperature techniques.

The need for thermodynamic data and information on properties of substances in general is well covered by other authors. One area I should like to emphasize concerns the properties of liquids at high temperature (and pressure). Most vapor-pressure studies stop at, or below, 1 atm. There is no sound basis for even estimating critical temperatures, much less other critical properties, of liquids other than molecular fluids—although Dr. Grosse (see page 58) discusses liquid metals. The chemistry of molten salts has received some attention of late; however, the liquid properties of the higher-melting substances such as oxides, sulfides, carbides, and the refractory metals are virtually unexplored. Since these are useful as structural materials, their melting processes and the melts themselves should be investigated. An interesting example of a serious gap in information is the almost complete lack of measured heats of fusion for metals melting above about 1,500° K. (Almost all values quoted are based on an assumed ΔS_f derived from lower-melting metals.) The main problem facing workers in this field is the container; increased effort on container studies would probably stimulate the whole field.

A general area in need of more attention is the kinetics and mechanism of high-temperature reactions—particularly those controlled by chemical processes. The kinetics of certain types of reactions are diffusion controlled. Thus, for example, the rates of most metal oxidations at high temperature are controlled by the diffusion of chemical species through the oxide layer; in flames, the diffusion species in the gas plays an important role in controlling the rate of combustion.

Thus, diffusion studies are important. Perhaps more important, and less well studied, is the kinetics of reactions controlled by processes that are fundamentally chemical in nature. In this group, I feel a distinction should be made between endothermic and exothermic reactions, primarily because the latter lead to reactions that are auto-accelerated to a degree dependent on the rate of heat removal. Of the former type, the kinetics of evaporation is an example. The kinetics of evaporation of solid metals has been studied somewhat; however, the influence of microstructure of the surface and specific types of surface defects, which are parameters that should seriously affect the kinetics, needs clarification. The kinetics of evaporation from liquid-metal surfaces should help in the understanding of solid evaporation. A related area is the mechanism of evaporation (or decomposition) of incongruently evaporating materials. In this case, the chemistry of the processes that regroup the species and result in incongruent evaporation (i.e., new species formed on evaporation) is an area the study of which should lead to understanding of the reactivities of high-temperature materials. Conversely, the kinetics of sticking of gases on reactive metals—or the mechanism of formation of the first few atomic layers of coatings on metals—needs attention (although there is work in progress in this field). Again, the influence of microstructure and surface-defect structure of the metal on the kinetics should be important and seems to be little studied.

The kinetics of reaction of exothermically decomposing substances is a little-understood area. The chemistry and mechanisms of such reactions should be explored as an aid to propulsion and explosives technology. The chemical mechanism of the decomposition of ammonium perchlorate, ammonium nitrate, alkali chlorates, and other more violently exploding or detonating substances is not understood, although descriptive studies have been made.

A somewhat different field is the chemistry and physics of changes that occur due to large temperature gradients. As an example of such conditions one can cite a high-temperature nuclear reactor of the type containing UC_2 fuel particles embedded in a graphite matrix. Along the radius of such a fuel particle there must be very large temperature gradients because of the extremely large heat fluxes out of the fuel particles into the graphite during operation. Such a temperature gradient can give rise to a composition gradient in the UC_2 particle and may influence its properties. There are no data available on which to base estimates of such an effect. Ablation is a field in which chemical changes are occurring in large heat fluxes, and it may be worth investigating whether any important coupling occurs between the heat flux and the chemical reactions occurring.

It is perhaps obvious, but worth restating, that advances in science are often the result of advances in instrumentation. Thus it may be scientifically productive to stimulate instrumentation for high-temperature research. Both the adaptation of existing instruments to high-temperature problems and the invention of new instruments should be encouraged.

QUESTION ADDRESSED TO DR. CUBICCIOTTI

QUESTION BY JOHN SLAUGHTER: If you need thermodynamic data on liquids at high temperatures and pressures, why not avoid the container problem by using high-pressure arcs and arc-image furnaces with molten material contained in water-cooled crucibles?

ANSWER: For many applications it is possible to avoid container problems by the method suggested; however, by its very nature the method involves large temperature gradients in the sample. I believe it would thus be difficult to measure with accuracy enthalpy changes or properties, like vapor pressure, that are very temperature dependent.

Status of High-Temperature Research

CHARLES W. BECKETT
National Bureau of Standards
Washington, D.C.

Fundamental problems in high-temperature chemistry are concerned largely with the structure and energy states, with transitions between such states, and with the relationship of structure to other properties, such as thermodynamic, transport, and kinetic properties. Having fairly complete structural information and sound theoretical methods, thermodynamic and transport properties of simple gases can be computed over a wide range of temperature at ordinary densities. However, for high densities, even for substances as simple as hydrogen and helium, one encounters difficulties because of insufficient information on intermolecular forces. Data are needed on properties over extended ranges of temperature and pressure, and better theoretical methods also are needed. Even more difficult problems exist with the more complex substances. Many of these are discussed in this volume.

Practical problems in high-temperature chemistry arise in diverse areas of research and technology. Some of these problem areas have become familiar—such as geochemistry, nuclear fission and fusion power, chemical rocket power, aerodynamic heating, and meteor and other hypervelocity impacts. Others are less generally known, such as exobiology, in which techniques of high-temperature chemistry are applied in the estimation of the occurrence of "ubiquitous" biological compounds, e.g., glycine, in other planets or more distant parts of the universe. Another is the prediction of the constituents of the interiors of planets from a rather limited amount of observational data and the equation of state of hydrogen, helium, water, methane, ammonia, iron, and several oxides (MgO, Al_2O_3, SiO_2). Pressures up to 2×10^7 atm are needed for this purpose. In this region, covalent bonding in hydrogen, water, and other materials has been replaced with metallic forces. Incidentally, one might speculate on the occurrence of the ubiquitous biological compounds in the million-atmosphere regions of some of the planets; but that is not really a practical problem.

The maximum theoretical strength of a substance is more important in a practical sense, particularly now since measured strengths of small fibers approach the theoretical limit closely in some cases. The limiting theoretical strength is closely related to the binding energy per unit volume, a quantity which is high in high-temperature materials; hence, a good correlation between high strength and high-temperature stability is not surprising.

In analyses of technical problems, essentially the same basic information (structural, thermodynamic, transport, and kinetic, for example) is required in virtually all applications of high-temperature processes and phenomena. The basic needs in specific technical areas can be characterized by the operating conditions (temperature, pressure, radiation, or other fields) and by a selection of elements and compounds relevant to the process. This selection usually has a crucial role in any new high-temperature development. Lack of reliable basic information upon which to base sound technical decisions has been costly in the past. Costly errors of this type can be minimized by systematic basic investigations of all technically important classes of substances. In a few cases, such as nuclear power and chemical propulsion, integrated research on a large group of properties of selected substances is yielding a fairly complete ensemble of basic data.

JANAF panel meetings, reviewing status and needs for thermodynamic and related properties of light element compounds, have occurred annually since 1958. The proceedings of these meetings contain critical summaries of many groups of substances and of many properties relevant to chemical propulsion. A close collaboration between research groups and development groups permitted assignment of priorities that have been followed consistently throughout most of the laboratories cooperating in that program. Significant advances in experimental techniques and improvements in thermodynamic tables available for analysis of performance of many propellant systems have occurred since the initiation of the JANAF program in 1958. However, even in this area the information is far from complete.

In other parts of the periodic table, the large voids in fundamental information, now experimentally accessible, could be filled with concerted effort during the next decade.

The above assertion is not sufficient to assure research at an adequate level. More tangible evidence of the need for the research on important technical problems is needed now. The most important problem confronting high-temperature chemists today is finding that evidence. A systematic study of technical requirements for basic data in many applied fields could provide a convincing program plan.

Containment of Liquid Metals
at High Temperatures
and the Estimation of Their Properties

A. V. GROSSE
The Research Institute of Temple University
Philadelphia, Pennsylvania

High-temperature chemistry is a challenging frontier for both science
and technology. The Temple University Research Institute has conducted research in this field for nearly 20 years. Since ordinary chemistry
"expires" at about 5,000°K due to thermal dissociation of all known
compounds, it is important to find substances that can be heated to
much higher temperatures and still remain in the condensed state.
It was found that the elementary refractory metals—such as tungsten,
rhenium, and tantalum—would remain liquid up to about 20,000°K.
Thus, provided the problem of containment can be solved, liquid metals
could be studied at temperatures far above the range used in current
experimentation. It is obvious that gases can be and have been heated
to very much higher temperatures without difficulty. Their containment
presents no problem since their density is of the order of a quarter of
a million times lower than that of heavy liquid metals.

It has been possible to contain liquid metallic substances at temperatures up to 5,000°K (1), by heating tantalum carbide in a subliming-
graphite stationary crucible or in a rotating pipe using a high-power
electric arc. Temperature was measured with an optical pyrometer,
its calibration being based on a National Bureau of Standards tungsten
band lamp. The highest temperature measured was 4,950 ± 50°K for
periods of 4 min. Longer runs, up to 0.5 hr were achieved subsequently.

In view of the possibility of liquid containment at much higher temperatures than heretofore, the important physical properties of liquid
metals became of interest to us and their estimation has become of
particular concern. It is obvious that it will be at least a few decades
until those properties can be measured, for many substances, over the
entire liquid range, that is, from the melting point to the critical point.

Thus, an estimation at this time, based on sound physical-chemical principles, is important.

Of primary importance, is the estimation of the critical temperatures of metals. In the past it has been assumed, in line with ordinary compounds, that the critical temperature is 1.5-1.75 times the normal boiling point in degrees Kelvin. It was found that the critical temperatures of metals are actually much higher. They can be estimated (2,4) by two independent methods, namely, the law of rectilinear diameters and the theorem of corresponding states. Usually, the two methods give consistent results.

The properties of interest to us are vapor pressure, density, viscosity, self-diffusion, surface tension and energy, electrical and thermal conductivities, and heat of vaporization. All these properties have been estimated for both the liquid and the saturated vapor phase, along the saturation line. The data for the liquid at the melting point are known for a large number of metals. The estimates for the saturated vapors can, in principle, be readily made by using a simple or more refined kinetic theory, since most of the vapors are essentially monatomic gases up to the critical region. It is important that the properties at the critical point can be approached <u>both</u> from the liquid and from the saturated vapor side. Thus, the critical point is an anchoring point, and since it is approached from both sides it can be more reliably estimated than if it were based on extrapolation to high temperatures alone.

VAPOR PRESSURE

The vapor pressure can be assumed to obey the Kirchhoff law, i.e.,

$$\log P = -(A/T) + B.$$

Although vapor-pressure curves have been expressed as equations containing up to five, and even six, constants, Edwards has shown (5) that for 30 inorganic substances—including the ideal monatomic liquids argon, krypton, and xenon—the maximum deviation from the Kirchhoff straight-line equation and the actual experimental values do not amount to more than 2.5 percent of the true vapor-pressure value. Thus, as a first approximation we use the straight-line relationship in the range from the normal boiling point to the critical point, estimated as mentioned above.

DENSITY

It has been shown (2,4) that the liquid density decreases linearly from the melting point* to the normal boiling point, i.e.,

$$D = D_0 - (dD/dT)\, T.$$

The law of rectilinear diameters has been demonstrated to be correct, at least in first approximation, all the way to the experimentally determined critical point in the case of mercury (F. Birch, 1932) and recently for cesium and rubidium as well. For temperatures above the boiling point, the density of the liquid can be obtained simply from the law of rectilinear diameters, since the actual saturated vapor density is very close to that of an ideal gas, which can be simply calculated. In the critical region, we have used the ratio of $D_L/D_{sat\ vap}$ versus T_{red} of an ideal liquid, such as argon, xenon, and krypton, as the first approximation for liquid metals. Thirty years ago, it was shown (6) that most liquids, except quantum liquids like helium and neon, are close to the noble-gas liquids with respect to this property.

VISCOSITY

The viscosities of liquid metals can be estimated readily by the so-called first (I) and second (II) Andrade equations (see references cited in references 7 and 8). The first equation,

$$\eta = ae^{H/RT}, \qquad \text{(I)}$$

can be used over a range of about $500°\,K$. The second equation,

$$\eta v^{1/3} = be^{c/vT}, \qquad \text{(II)}$$

takes into consideration the change of specific volume with temperature; this becomes important when covering the whole range from the melting point to the critical point. Andrade has shown that his equation II applies for all substances that he investigated over the whole range from the melting point to the critical point. We have found, further, that an empirical relationship exists between Andrade's activation energy, $H\eta$, and the absolute melting point of the metal (7,8) as follows:

* The density of a liquid metal at its melting point can be estimated from the x-ray data for the solid at room temperature in combination with expansion data for metals of the same group in the Periodic Table. The volume change on fusion is nearly always positive and equals on the average $+3.6$ percent. Exceptions are Bi (-3.3 percent), Ga (-3.1 percent), Sb (-0.94 percent, and Pu.

$$H\eta \text{ (in cal/g-at)} = 0.431 \ T_{m.p.}^{1.348} \text{ (in } °K).$$

Since the density or the specific volume can be estimated all the way to the critical point (as discussed in the preceding section), it is possible to use Andrade's equation II to estimate η all the way to the critical point, as has been demonstrated for mercury (9) and for sodium and potassium (10). In addition, on the basis of well-known data, Andrade has given the following simple expression for estimating the viscosity at the melting point:

$$\eta_{m.p.} = 5.7 \times 10^{-4} \left[(A_{wt} \ T_{m.p.})^{1/2} \Big/ V_{A \text{ at m.p.}}^{2/3} \right].$$

Thus, by using all the above equations, coupled with simple kinetic theory data for the saturated vapor, it is possible to estimate the viscosity up to the critical point for practically any metal. Since both the viscosity and the density can be estimated for most metals, the kinematic viscosity or the reduced kinematic (11) viscosity can be estimated also. It is of interest that liquid metals (12) differ markedly from van der Waals or covalent substances (like Ar and H_2O) in that, throughout a substantial temperature range far below the critical temperature, the kinematic viscosities show pronounced minima. In the case of mercury, cesium, rubidium, potassium, and sodium, the minimum should be within the present experimental range, and thus can be expected to be demonstrated in the near future.

SELF-DIFFUSION

Since the self-diffusion coefficient, D, is closely related to the viscosity by the Stokes-Einstein relation, i.e.,

$$\eta D = kT/6\delta,$$

where δ is the average distance between atoms, we can easily obtain D, provided both η and D are expressed in a self-consistent manner (13). Using the simple Frenkel theory, η and D can be expressed as follows (13):

$$\eta = BTe^{-\gamma}e^{+E_{VD}/RT}$$

and

$$D = D_0 e^{\gamma} e^{-E_{VD}/RT},$$

where

and

$$B = hN_A \big/ \theta_D V_A,$$

$$D_0 = \left(\frac{k}{6hN_A{}^{2/3}}\right)\theta_D V_A{}^{2/3} .$$

In these formulas, e^γ and $e^{-\gamma} \simeq 1$; h, k, and N_A are the Planck and Boltzmann constants and Avogadro's number; θ_D is the Debye temperature; and V_A the atomic volume. The activation energy for viscosity and diffusion, E_{VD}, is:

$$E_{VD} \ (\text{cal}/\text{g-at}) = 3.53 \ T_{m.p.}^{1.10} \ (T \ \text{in} \ {}^\circ\text{K}) .$$

SURFACE TENSION

If the critical temperature T_c of the metal is known, the surface tension can be assumed, in first approximation, to be a straight-line function, as follows:

$$\sigma = \sigma^\circ - \sigma^\circ \ (T/T_c),$$

where σ° is the surface tension of the liquid extrapolated to 0°K; $\sigma = 0$ at T_c. An empirical relationship has been found (14) between the surface tension at the melting point, $\sigma_{m.p.}$, the heat of vaporization, ΔH_V, and the atomic volume, V_A. For cubic and tetragonal metals

$$\sigma_{m.p.} = 0.274 \left(\frac{\Delta H_V \ \text{at m.p.}}{V_A \ \text{at m.p.}}\right)^{0.934} ,$$

and for hexagonal and rhombohedral metals

$$\sigma_{m.p.} = 5.740 \left(\frac{\Delta H_V \ \text{at m.p.}}{V_A \ \text{at m.p.}}\right)^{0.620} .$$

Furthermore, it was found (14) that the surface-free energy at the melting point, $F_{m.p.}^\sigma$, for cubic and tetragonal metals equals 15 percent of their heat of vaporization at the melting point, i.e.,

$$F_{m.p.}^\sigma = 0.15 \ (\Delta H_V \ \text{at m.p.}).$$

ELECTRICAL CONDUCTIVITY

A simple hyperbolic relationship has been found (15,17) between the electrical conductivity of a metal and temperature over its entire liquid range. This relationship can be expressed in a simple manner if the temperature of the metal is defined in a reduced form, i.e.,

$$\theta = (T - T_{m.p.}) / (T_c - T_{m.p.})$$

Thus, θ equals 0 at the melting point and 1 at the critical point. The conductivity, $\varkappa$, is also defined in the reduced form,

$$\varkappa_{red.} = \varkappa_T / \varkappa_{m.p.}$$

The hyperbolic relationship is as follows:

$$(\varkappa_{red.} + b)(\theta + b) = b(1 + b)$$

or

$$\varkappa_{red.} = b(1 - \theta) / (b + \theta) ,$$

where b is a constant for the metal.

This relationship is based on the actual experimental measurements for mercury from the melting point to the critical point and for the alkali metals, cesium, rubidium, and sodium over a substantial part of their liquid ranges. Of all metals for which conductivity data are available, lithium seems to be the only one at present for which this relationship is not valid in the simple form given above.

THERMAL CONDUCTIVITY

The thermal conductivity, λ_{therm}, can be expressed (18,20) in the simplest manner by the Wiedemann-Franz law, namely:

$$\lambda_{therm} = L\varkappa T,$$

where L is the Lorentz number, $\varkappa$ the electrical conductivity, and T the absolute temperature.

HEAT OF VAPORIZATION

The heat of vaporization can be expressed over the whole liquid range from the melting point to the critical point in terms of θ (see the section on Electrical Conductivity, page 62), as follows:

$$\Delta H_v = \Delta H_{m.p.} (1 - \theta)^a ,$$

where a is the constant for each metal. In the case of van der Waals substances, a = 0.38 for most of them, as has been shown by K. W. Watson and others decades ago.

In summary, the above relationships permit one to estimate the physical properties listed over the entire liquid temperature range for any elementary metal. A number of other properties, which can be derived from those listed, can also be estimated.

REFERENCES

1. A. V. Grosse, "Containment of Liquid Metallic Substances up to 5,000°K," Part III of lecture given at the Colloque International de Chimie des Hautes Temperature, Paris, France, June 29, 1965. Revue Internationale des Hautes Temperatures et des Refractaires.
2. A. V. Grosse, "Liquid Range of Metals and Some of Their Physical Properties at High Temperatures," Research Institute of Temple University, Philadelphia, Pa., September 5, 1960.
3. A. V. Grosse, J. Inorg. Nucl. Chem., 22, 23 (1961).
4. A. V. Grosse, Science, 140, 781 (1963).
5. D. G. Edwards, Rept. UCRL 7167, Lawrence Radiation Laboratory, University of California (June 13, 1963).
6. H. Fales and C. Shapiro, J. Am. Chem. Soc., 58, 2418 (1936).
7. A. V. Grosse, J. Inorg. Nucl. Chem., 23, 333 (1961).
8. A. V. Grosse, J. Inorg. Nucl. Chem., 25, 317 (1963).
9. A. V. Grosse, J. Phys. Chem., 68, 3419 (1964).
10. A. V. Grosse, Science, 147, 1438 (1965).
11. A. V. Grosse, J. Inorg. Nucl. Chem., 27, 979 (1965).
12. A. V. Grosse, J. Inorg. Nucl. Chem., in press.
13. A. V. Grosse, Science, 145, 50 (1964).
14. A. V. Grosse, J. Inorg. Nucl. Chem., 26, 1349 (1964).
15. A. V. Grosse, "Simple Relationship between Electrical Conductivity of Liquid Metals and Temperature over Their Entire Liquid Range . . . ," Research Institute of Temple University, Philadelphia, Pa., Nov. 22, 1964.
16. A. V. Grosse, J. Inorg. Nucl. Chem., in press.
17. A. V. Grosse, "Electrical and Thermal Conductivities of Metals over Their Entire Liquid Range . . . " (Part I) Revue Internationale des Hautes Temperatures et des Refractaires, in press.
18. A. V. Grosse, "Thermal Conductivity of Liquid Metals over Their Entire Liquid Range . . . ," Research Institute of Temple University, Philadelphia, Pa., December 7, 1964.
19. A. V. Grosse, J. Inorg. Nucl. Chem., in press.
20. A. V. Grosse, "Thermal Conductivity of Liquid Metals from the Melting Point to the Critical Point . . . " (Part II) Revue Internationale des Hautes Temperatures et des Refractaires, in press.

High Temperatures, High Pressures, and Periodic Compounds

H. TRACY HALL
Brigham Young University
Provo, Utah

High-pressure research has grown at an explosive rate during the past several years (probably 1,000 papers now appear per year whereas 10 years ago there were almost none). Impetus for this spurt was, no doubt, engendered by the synthesis of diamond, announced in 1955. At that time there were generous predictions that the high-pressure high-temperature techniques used to make diamonds would soon be used to synthesize many new, interesting, exotic, and useful materials. The results have been disappointing. True, there have been coesite (actually made before diamonds), stishovite (or popovavite), and borazon; but beyond these and a few other examples, there has been little to excite the imagination. What are the reasons for this? The primary reason is that synthesis·of new materials is difficult. Furthermore, there have been few guidelines or concepts to suggest what might be synthesized. Then there are the questions of what starting materials, pressure, temperature, and time to use and what solvent or catalyst is needed. When a new substance is made, it is usually made only in milligram quantities (due to the small size of the reaction chambers generally available) and, in addition, it is usually contaminated with other products, which makes separation and identification difficult.

When it comes right down to it, it is much easier to make some kind of physical measurement at high pressure than it is to synthesize a new substance. When a measurement is made, there is bound to be some kind of data collected that can be published: this may explain why the vast majority of papers on high-pressure research being published today are indeed concerned with measurement of some property.

It would seem important to put some additional effort into the area of chemical synthesis, particularly of inorganic materials. Such materials can be scientifically interesting, important to additional understanding of the solid state of matter, and may, in addition, be technologically useful.

A new concept that I have recently developed, the concept of "periodic compounds," should be useful in predicting the formulas of some compounds that might be synthesized by high-pressure high-temperature techniques. In addition, I have succeeded in synthesizing (by high-pressure high-temperature means) the interesting group IV periodic compound B_2O, an analog of carbon.

A periodic compound is a combination of elements in which the average number of bonding electrons per atom is an integer corresponding to one of the periodic groups I, II, III, IV . . . . Such compounds may be defined by the expression $\bar{G} = \Sigma d_i e_i / \Sigma d_i$, where $\bar{G}$ assumes the integral values 1, 2, 3, 4, . . . corresponding to the periodic groups. The number of bonding electrons contributed by an atom of kind i is given by e_i, and the number of atoms of kind i participating in the bond, per unit formula, is given by d_i. Both e_i and d_i assume integral values. In the expression above, when $\bar{G}$ is permitted to range from 2 through 6, e_i from 1 through 7, and i from 1 through 2, the general chemical formulas for 35 compounds are generated. These are binary compounds, i.e., they contain two different kinds of atoms. When i is allowed to range from 1 through 3 (three kinds of atoms in the chemical formula) and the range of $\bar{G}$ and e_i is the same as above, the general formulas of 105 ternary compounds are generated. Considering the eight sequences in the periodic table in which the "normal" electron configurations increase from 1 to 7 (groups I through VII) on passing from lower to higher atomic number, the chemical formulas of over 500 binary periodic compounds and over 13,000 ternary compounds can be written. The synthesis of many of these periodic compounds, judging from electronegativity and metallicity considerations, should be possible. High pressure should prove efficacious in this connection.

The synthesis of a number of periodic compounds, particularly those of group IV with low values of average principal quantum number, $\bar{n}$, and electronegativity difference, ΔX, should be of particular interest. This could include such substances as B_2S, B_2Se, B_2Te, B_2Cr, B_3Mn, B_3I, BeP_2, B_3Br, B_3Cl, and BeN_2. None of these compounds is known to exist. If they can be synthesized, they should be hard abrasive substances possessing semiconducting properties. Their hardness should rank them among those of the seven hardest known compounds (AlB_{12}, boron, cubic BN, B_4C, diamond, SiC, and TiB_2).

Vapor–Solid Transformations: Nucleation and Growth

S. J. HRUSKA
Purdue University
Lafayette, Indiana

The initial stages of the formation of a solid at a vapor - solid interface can be described in terms of heterogeneous nucleation theory,
treating the adsorbed but not condensed species as a system in metastable equilibrium. Such analysis has been successfully applied to the
initial reaction occurring during vapor deposition of materials in thin-
film formation and to the growth behavior of crystals at low supersat-
urations.

FORMATION OF SOLID ON FOREIGN SUBSTRATE

When a vapor impinges on a solid at a flux, J_i, the emerging flux, J_{em},
can be equal to it prior to the formation of stable growing clusters of
the vapor material. The emerging flux is composed of those species
that are simply reflected by the substrate and of those that emerge
from an adsorbed state. Fluctuations in the adsorbate lead to stable
clusters; when these clusters are present in sufficient number,
$J_{em} < J_i$ and can become negligible. The rate at which these clusters
form, expressed in terms of number per unit area per unit time, is
the nucleation rate and can be formulated in a manner similar to the
classical theory for vapor - liquid homogeneous nucleation. Pound
et al.(1), following the Vollmer model of a cap-shaped cluster of adsorbate, formulated an expression for the areal concentration of clusters of various sizes employing the van't Hoff isotherm. Macroscopic
thermodynamic properties are ascribed to the clusters, and all clusters of the "critical" size or smaller are considered to be in thermal
equilibrium with the substrate, at temperature T_s, and in metastable
chemical equilibrium with one another. The rate at which clusters   67

grow through this critical size, the nucleation rate, is taken to be the product of the concentration of such critical sized clusters and the rate at which monomeric species impinge on them. The theoretical prediction is that the rate of nucleation is a sharp function of the impinging flux, J_i, for a given substrate temperature, T_s, and also a sharp function of T_s for given J_i. This behavior is in accord with experimental observations of Knudsen (2), Cockcroft (3), Yang et al. (4), and current workers (5). Also, experimental data, in most cases, are described by the relation

$$T_s^3 [\ln(J_i / J_e)]^2 = \text{constant}$$

for a given nucleation rate, where J_e is the flux that would emerge from a crystal of the vapor material in chemical equilibrium at T_s. This relation is appropriate for the cap-shaped cluster model. Further, field electron emission observations by Moazed (6) and by Gretz (7) in cases where the vapors strongly adsorb and the condition $J_i = J_{em}$ is not attainable have confirmed that metastable equilibrium obtains between monomers and clusters. Other cluster shapes have been considered, and formulations employing statistical mechanics (8) have been developed.

The available data pertain to systems where the vapors are not reflected and where thermal accommodation of the adsorbate is likely. Some anomalous vapor deposition behavior is believed to be due to thermal nonaccommodation. Vapor sources at higher temperatures could give rise to situations where reflection of the impinging species is likely, whereupon

$$T_s^3 [\ln(kJ_i / J_e)]^2 = \text{constant},$$

where k is the fraction of impinging species which adsorb, should be applicable. This is appropriate for thermally accommodated adsorbate. When thermal accommodation is not complete, the kinetic formulation which deals with clusters that are in metastable equilibrium is not applicable, and a suggested approach is the treatment of the formation of stable clusters as the result of clusters passing through a size-energy space in the manner of Russell et al. (9).

CRYSTAL GROWTH AT LOW SUPERSATURATIONS

In the theory of crystal growth from the vapor, the rate of addition of material, R, is given by the difference between the impinging and emerging fluxes, J_i and J_{em}:

$$R = J_i - J_{em}.$$

According to the theoretical work of Burton et al. (10), when growth sites on the crystal surface are sufficiently numerous J_{em} equals the flux J_e which would impinge on the crystal if it were maintained at equilibrium:

$$R = (J_i - J_e)\alpha$$

or in terms of the kinetic theory of gases

$$R = (P_i - P_e)\alpha/(2\pi kT)^{1/2} \; ,$$

where in this case the condensation coefficient $\alpha = 1$. When growth sites are separated by distances much greater than the root-mean-square diffusion distance of the adsorbed species during its stay time, $\alpha < 1$ and is determined by the mobility of adsorbed but not condensed species on the regions of surface that are free of growth sites.

Crystal surfaces that are not smooth, possibly due to the emergence of line imperfections, are likely to lead to $\alpha = 1$ for all P_i, while smooth surfaces of the close-packed low-index type that are free of imperfections may have $\alpha \leq 1$ depending on the magnitude of P_j. The relative magnitude of P_i governs the probability of the spontaneous formation of growth sites. These sites are present at the edges of monatomically high clusters which can nucleate in the adsorbed population on smooth surfaces. The formulation of this kinetic process follows the same reasoning as for the nucleation considered in the preceding section. Here, the nucleation rate is the rate at which disk-like clusters of adsorbate grow through a critical size (11). This geometrical assignment leads to the theoretical prediction that

$$T_s^2 \ln(P_i/P_e) = \text{constant}$$

for a given nucleation rate, where P_i/P_e is the supersaturation ratio, and that the rate of nucleation is a sharp function of P_i for a given T_s, increasing with P_i, and a sharp function of T_s for a given P_i, increasing as T_s decreases. Accordingly, the prediction is that $\alpha \ll 1$ for P_i less than some critical value $P_{i,c}$, while $\alpha = 1$ when P_i is greater. At $P_i < P_{i,c}$, α is determined by the kinetics of adsorption, surface migration, and incorporation of adsorbed species into growth sites (5).

The anisotropic growth of crystals studied by Sears (12) and the kinetics of whisker growth studied by Dittmar and Neumann (13) illustrate the dependence of growth rate on supersaturation and crystal perfection. At pressures less than $P_{i,c}$, regions of crystal that present growth sites are described by $\alpha = 1$, while more perfect regions involve $\alpha < 1$ and also serve to supply the former regions with material via surface migration, giving rise to anisotropic growth.

Growth at pressures on the order of $P_{i,c}$ usually does not involve vapor source temperatures much greater than the crystal temperature, hence thermal accommodation is assumed. In situations where the vapor source is held at a much higher temperature, as in directed beam studies, thermal nonaccommodation would affect $P_{i,c}$ and hence α. Also growth at $P_i > P_{i,c}$, where net condensation may be quite high, might involve kinetics on a surface whose temperature is significantly increased on exposure to vapor.

REFERENCES

1. G. M. Pound, M. T. Simnad, and L. Yang, J. Chem. Phys., 22, 1215 (1954).
2. M. Knudsen, Ann. Phys., 48, 1113 (1915).
3. J. D. Cockcroft, Proc. Roy. Soc. (London), 119A, 293 (1923).
4. L. Yang, C. E. Birchenal, G. M. Pound, and M. T. Simnad, Acta Met., 2, 462 (1954).
5. J. P. Hirth and G. M. Pound, Condensation and Evaporation, Nucleation and Growth Kinetics, Pergamon, New York (1963).
6. K. L. Moazed, Doctoral Thesis, Carnegie Institute of Technology (1960).
7. R. D. Gretz and G. M. Pound, in Condensation and Evaporation of Solids, E. Rutner, P. Goldfinger, and J. P. Hirth, eds., Gordon and Breach, New York (1964), p. 575.
8. J. P. Hirth, Ann. N.Y. Acad. Sci., 101, 805 (1963).
9. K. C. Russell, J. Lothe, and G. M. Pound, in Condensation and Evaporation of Solids, E. Rutner, P. Goldfinger, and J. P. Hirth, eds., Gordon and Breach, New York (1964), p. 503.
10. W. K. Burton, N. Cabrera, and F. C. Frank, Phil. Trans. Roy. Soc. (London), A243, 299 (1950).
11. J. P. Hirth, Acta Met., 7, 755 (1959).
12. G. W. Sears, Acta Met., 3, 367 (1955).
13. W. Dittmar and K. Neumann, Z. Elektrochem., 64, 297 (1960).

QUESTIONS ADDRESSED TO DR. HRUSKA

QUESTION BY JOHN L. MARGRAVE: Is thermal accommodation better on a foreign substrate or on an identical substrate?

ANSWER: This question has not been answered experimentally and only partially answered theoretically.

The calculation of the energy transfer when an atom impinges on a substrate and the binding energy is at least kT has been limited to simplified models in which a one-dimensional semi-infinite chain of spring-connected masses is envisaged. Such calculations by McCarroll and Ehrlich [J. Chem. Phys., 38, 523 (1963)] lead to the prediction that the probability of capture on impact and subsequent thermal accommodation increases as the binding energy increases. Accordingly, the thermal accommodation of an atom on a substrate of its own kind is greater or less than on a foreign substrate depending on whether the binding energy to the foreign substrate is greater or less than about one half the heat of sublimation of the atom from a crystal of its own kind.

QUESTION BY JOHN L. MARGRAVE: Is anything known about the temperature coefficient of the thermal accommodation coefficient?

ANSWER: I am not aware of any relevant experimental work.

Gas-Solid Reactions
in Flow Environments at High Temperatures

EARL A. GULBRANSEN
Westinghouse Research Laboratories
Pittsburgh, Pennsylvania

One of the characteristic features of the oxidation of high-temperature materials is the formation of volatile reaction products. Since the protective oxide films are not present on the surface, the mechanisms of oxidation are different from classical mechanisms of oxidation. Fast oxidation reactions occur. One of our major tasks is to separate the various processes experimentally so that the individual processes can be studied.

Six rate-controlling processes occur in the over-all mechanism of oxidation of metals under conditions where volatile oxides are formed. These are:

1. Transport of oxygen gas through a barrier layer of volatilized oxide vapors
2. Chemisorption of oxygen
3. Chemical reaction
4. Desorption of volatile oxide
5. Transport of volatilized oxide away from the surface
6. Spalling

Processes 1 and 5 are gas-transport processes. If rate-controlling, the temperature dependence of the reaction rate would vary as a small power of the absolute temperature. Chemical reactions 2, 3, and 4 usually have high activation energies. The temperature dependence allows one to distinguish chemical reactions from gas transport processes. In addition, the values of the activation energy and the pressure dependence allow one to distinguish the several chemical processes.

Table 1 shows six high-temperature elements that form volatile oxides when the element is reacted with oxygen. The volatile oxide and the temperature for forming the oxide are given. Experimentally,

C, Re, and Mo are best suited for studying the kinetics of these special oxidizing reactions since relatively low-temperature conditions can be used. At temperatures above $1,500\,^\circ C$, oxygen begins to dissociate and the experimental procedures become more complex. C, even in its most dense form, is porous, which adds an element of uncertainty in kinetic studies.

Thermochemical analyses can be made of the various oxidizing reactions and of all possible side reactions, since many obscure reactions can occur at high temperature. In flow environments, thermochemical calculations must be used with caution since the reaction conditions are far from equilibrium and it is difficult to define the actual oxidizing conditions.

To define the oxidizing conditions of the elements given in Table 1, it is necessary to specify the temperature, pressure, gas composition, gas flow, sample size, and geometry of the reaction system. Since the products of reaction accumulate rapidly around the specimen in a static reaction system, flow-type reaction systems are essential for the experimental study of these fast reactions.

A brief description of a flow-type reaction system used in our laboratories will be given. Automated microbalances and gas-handling apparatus are essential since short reaction times must be used. Special consideration must be given to the purity of the solid and the reacting gas. Also, special care must be taken to monitor the reaction gas in the furnace system to avoid contaminants.

Our method incorporates an automatic recording vacuum microbalance having a sensitivity of 10^{-7} g per mm deflection, a period of

TABLE 1. Temperatures for Forming Volatile Oxides

Element	Melting Point ($^\circ$C)	Boiling Point ($^\circ$C)	Volatile Oxide	Temperature for Forming Volatile Oxide ($^\circ$C)
C	$3,652$[a]	$4,200$	CO	425[c]
Re	$3,167$	$5,900$[b]	Re_2O_7	600[c]
Mo	$2,620$	$4,507$	$(MoO_3)_3$	800[c]
W	$3,410$	$5,900$	$(WO_3)_3$	$1,200$[c]
Nb	$2,415$	$3,300$	NbO	$1,700$[d]
Ta	$2,996$	$6,000$[b]	TaO	$2,200$[b]

[a] Sublimes.

[b] Estimated.

[c] From kinetic measurements.

[d] From phase diagrams.

less than 0.1 sec, and a sample weight change of 1 g on a 1-g sample. Pressures could be varied between 10^{-4} and 10^2 torr. Gas flow was controlled automatically using an ion gauge, a Pirani gauge, and a capacitance manometer as sensors and a servo-controlled leak valve.

Rapid and precise control of pressure and gas flow rates allows us to maintain the environment constant around the specimen. Flow rates between 10^{15} and 10^{20} molecules of oxygen per second and temperatures up to 1,650°C were used. For these conditions, it was possible to evaluate the flow and kinetic theory efficiencies of the reaction and to study the transition between gas-diffusion-controlled reactions and chemical-controlled reactions. Good kinetic data as a function of temperature and pressure also allow one to evaluate the particular type of chemical rate-controlling mechanism of reaction.

The oxidation of Re and Mo are used to illustrate the type of information one can obtain in kinetic studies at high temperature. The studies were made over the temperature range 600-1,600°C and for oxygen pressures of 5×10^{-4} torr to 76 torr.

The rates of oxidation of Re and Mo were found to be nearly linear functions of time. The chemically controlled region of oxidation was distinguished from the oxygen-gas-diffusion region of oxidation by plotting the kinetic data on a log rate versus $1/T$ plot. For both Mo and Re, a transition to gas-diffusion-controlled oxidation occurred at a rate of oxidation of about 10^{18} atoms of Mo or Re/cm^2-sec. The transition temperatures for Re and Mo were 1,100°C and 1,500°C, respectively, for the flow conditions and sample sizes used.

Flow efficiencies of 25 percent for the oxidation of Re were obtained at 1,500°C and 2-torr oxygen pressure and a kinetic theory efficiency of 0.5 percent.

For the chemically controlled region of oxidation, enthalpies of activation of 21 kcal/mole and 19.7 kcal/mole were calculated for the oxidation of Re and Mo, respectively. The values for the enthalpies of activation support an oxygen adsorption process as the rate-limiting step in the over-all oxidation mechanisms.

A short summary of the problem of protecting materials at high temperatures will be given. Special coatings and alloying additions may be used to overcome partially one or more of the many factors responsible for poor oxidation performance at high temperature. One of the major problems will be to overcome the thermodynamic and kinetically favorable processes of forming volatile oxides.

This work was supported in part by the U.S. Army Research Office, Durham, North Carolina.

QUESTION ADDRESSED TO DR. GULBRANSEN

QUESTION BY R. H. FOX: What is the state of our knowledge regarding transport of oxygen through oxide or other protective coatings on refractory substrates at temperatures above 2,000°K?

ANSWER: Very little work exists in the published literature on the transport of oxygen through oxide or other protective coatings on refractory substrates above 2,000°K. Visual observation of samples under test is not very satisfactory. Time to failure, as estimated from visible coating breakdown, is subject to many difficulties including coating defects, irregularities, and nonuniformity of thickness.

Measurement of oxygen transport is very difficult due to the complex series of reactions that occur at 2,000°K. Oxygen can dissolve in the metal phase, form an oxide, or volatilize. Each of these processes has to be evaluated to determine the transport of oxygen through the protective coatings or oxide films.

For further information one can refer to a book by Dr. Per Kofstad titled High Temperature Oxidation of Metals to be published by Wiley for the Electrochemical Society.

Problems in High-Temperature Chemistry

GEORGE B. RATHMANN
Minnesota Mining and Manufacturing Company
Saint Paul, Minnesota

INTRODUCTION

At temperatures above $2,500\,°K$ lies a vast area of chemistry that is orders of magnitude more difficult to study than are chemical phenomena under conventional conditions. Such study is further hampered by the fact that our intuitive concepts of heat transfer, mass transfer, reaction rates, and the nature of chemical bonds themselves, are generally inapplicable or misleading at these high temperatures. Because only limited funds and effort can be directed into any research area, it is important to find the most efficient means of acquiring the necessary information.

One approach is to give priority to the study of a few chemical species and properties within specific temperature ranges, based on needs as they can be currently defined. This approach introduces the risk that potentially fruitful areas may not be adequately explored for new leads because of overemphasis on areas of former significance. It may be desirable to temper such an approach by simultaneous emphasis on the definition of broad general methods of acquiring data, making correlations, and ultimately developing powerful general theoretical treatments from which specific predictions can be made.

An example of the successful use of this approach is the application of the equilibrium-shift technique to the field of high-speed reactions. (This technique may or may not be applicable in the field of high-temperature chemistry, however.) Before this innovation, rate constants of high-speed reactions were generally measured by extrapolation to short reaction times, by observing rates at low temperature and extrapolating from these to temperatures of interest, or by other techniques with limited accuracy, involving tedious experimentation, and generally with severe limitations because of, for example, mixing times.

A comparable contribution to the field of high-temperature chemistry might be the definition of an experimental approach to the automatic monitoring of high-temperature equilibria, reaction rates, or transport properties of systems in containerless surroundings. Ideally, such data might be acquired simultaneously at many temperatures or at least readily over a broad temperature range.

Because progress toward the development of generalized methods and theories will take considerable time, we should consider those urgent problem areas currently confronting us. The following is a brief summary of some specific problems concerning measurements and standards, gas-phase and solid-state systems, and the utilization of high-temperature synthesis.

MEASUREMENTS AND STANDARDS

The problems of defining a high-temperature scale and of standardization of reporting information have been discussed in the past by the Committee on High-Temperature Chemical Phenomena. Specific needs for additional high-temperature information and measurements include:

1. A definitive text on experimental high-temperature work comparable to the two volumes of Experimental Thermochemistry, issued in 1956 and 1962 as the direct result of a project started in 1949 by the IUPAC Commission on Thermochemistry.

2. Container materials for conducting high-temperature studies and reactions; better characterization of the physical and chemical stabilities of metals and ceramics would assist in the selection of suitable candidates.

3. Apparatus for studies of thermodynamic properties conducted simultaneously at high temperatures (above $1,500\,^{\circ}K$) and high pressures (above 100 kb).

4. Information on high-temperature energy-transfer rates and mechanisms and on high-temperature kinetics, required for increasing applications; specific chemical systems are being studied, but a general new approach to acquiring this type of data in a more automated way and with greater precision is needed.

5. High-temperature phase-diagram information on metals and ceramic systems.

GAS-PHASE PROBLEMS

Principal technological areas for which additional data on gaseous species are needed are chemical propulsion, chemical explosives, and, to some degree, ion propulsion. The coating and cladding of materials from vapor-phase reactions are conducted largely on an empirical basis because of the lack of data.

Some specific areas needing additional effort include:

1. Heavy elements, frequently neglected because of the emphasis on elements useful for chemical propellants.

2. Chemical kinetics, for which specific data are needed, as well as more powerful theoretical approaches for reducing data on the kinetics of propellant and explosive reactions for handling by computers.

3. Thermodynamics at high temperatures and pressures. The need for additional data in this area would be partially alleviated if improved equations of state could be defined with applicability to these conditions.

4. Kinetics in the presence of a solid phase, which has special importance in many combustion problems and in the preparation and fabrication of high-temperature materials and coatings.

5. The chemistry of low-lying excited electronic states, an area of chemistry that has not been investigated extensively and that may be important to reaction kinetics.

SOLID-STATE PROBLEMS

Requirements are increasing for materials that can be used for extended periods at high temperatures, including materials of construction, semiconductors, and thermoelectric devices. Most suitable systems are arrived at by extensive empirical evaluations. Little information is available for predicting the utility of such systems or for suggesting approaches to minimize deteriorations. The kinetics of grain growth, heterogeneous reaction, and phase changes and the development of measurements and generalized theoretical approaches for predicting transport properties are areas in which potentially important contributions can be made.

In the field of high-temperature burners, some special problems exist, including the need for emissivity data and better means for rapidly estimating temperature.

With regard to the cladding of metals and ceramics, there is inadequate understanding of the wetting and adhesion of two materials. Detailed studies of surfaces created under ideal conditions and of compound formation across an interface might bring new insight concerning interfacial reactions and welding and adhesion phenomena at high temperatures.

In the field of high-temperature protective coatings, predictions of performance are hampered by the lack of thermal conductivity data. Special problems exist concerning the transient ablative materials currently used and in many systems involving substantially longer terms of exposure, in which the dynamic heat-transfer situation persists.

HIGH-TEMPERATURE SYNTHESIS

A number of publications in recent years have illustrated the important potential of utilizing high temperatures with rapid quenching for the preparation of covalently bonded carbon compounds, including C_3 derivatives, tetrafluorethylene, and xylene derivatives. By somewhat different methods, a large number of high-temperature stable and semiconducting polymers have been prepared. This field offers the potential for discovering many new compounds and, with the introduction of hetero atoms, the possibility for new types and classes of bonds. Process engineering studies to scale up some of these systems might lead to the definition of important needs for basic high-temperature data, as well as to the development of new methods for handling extreme pressure and temperature gradients on a practical scale.

The Chemistry of Hot and Cold Plasmas

R. F. BADDOUR
Department of Chemical Engineering
Massachusetts Institute of Technology
Cambridge, Massachusetts

Chemical synthesis in gas plasmas has been of great interest to industry for many years. After the first World War, for example, plasma chemistry provided the only significant route to synthetic fixed nitrogen in this country, by means of a process the development of which extended back to the nineteenth century. In plasma chemical synthesis, the interest lies primarily in: producing old materials more efficiently and synthesizing new materials. Research in this laboratory has been carried on in both areas with successful results.

High-temperature plasmas (gas temperatures in excess of about 3,000° K) have many interesting and useful properties. Any desired elements can be maintained in the vapor phase; reaction rates are rapid, interesting equilibrium distributions are obtained, and, using electric power sources, large quantities of materials may be processed in a small unit.

Important commercial applications of high-temperature processing are sure to increase. However, there are some serious drawbacks to using high gas temperatures. Plasma confinement creates problems and introduces inefficiencies. Contamination from electrodes is inevitable, except in the relatively small number of cases where the electrode material is the same as that of one of the reactants. The gases must be quenched in order to preserve or produce the desired products, resulting in considerable loss of high-temperature energy.

Many of these problems may be overcome by using a cold plasma to produce high-energy gas species. (Cold plasma has low gas temperature, but high electron temperature; for this discussion, the hot plasma will be designated an arc and the cold plasma will be termed a discharge.) These discharges may be obtained in the absence of electrodes, at quite low gas temperatures, and with essentially complete coupling between the power source and the plasma. It has already been shown that a number of reactions that proceed only with great difficulty in the absence of a plasma (high temperature, catalyst, or both) proceed quite easily in a discharge. Further, at least one new material has been synthesized and identified in a microwave discharge. This area appears to be quite fruitful for rapid exploitation in the near future.

There are some serious drawbacks to discharges. They must be operated at low pressure (less than about 0.5 atm, typically below 0.1 atm) in order to maintain the low gas temperature. This makes scale-up to large production units especially difficult and severely limits the through-put for a given unit. The power sources contribute significantly to the processing cost, so that this technique will be restricted, at least in the early applications, to relatively expensive chemicals.

Further, many important phenomena associated with the electric discharge are poorly understood. The mechanism by which the energy is transferred to the plasma is not understood in sufficient detail to estimate the maximum over-all efficiency that may be achieved in converting electric power to chemical energy. The mechanism by which the high-energy species combine to produce the desired end products is also poorly understood. In particular, the degree to which the combination may be controlled by the use of solid catalysts is almost completely unknown.

In summary, both hot and cold plasmas have specific advantages and limitations for chemical synthesis. Some of these limitations appear to be inherent in the properties of these plasmas, but others result from an ignorance of many of their properties and should be eliminated by appropriate research.

Future Investigations in High-Temperature Chemistry Suggested by Vaporization Studies

PAUL W. GILLES
Department of Chemistry
University of Kansas
Lawrence, Kansas

A high-temperature vaporization study can serve to obtain thermodynamic information for simple gaseous molecules and thermodynamic data for condensed refractory phases, to reveal the nature of high-temperature reactions, to yield vapor pressures of pure materials, to give partial molal free energies and enthalpies of the components in solutions and information about the kinetics and mechanisms of high-temperature reactions, to produce new compounds, and to prepare single crystals. Such a wealth of results raises many problems, and the purpose of the present report is to suggest some fruitful lines of future study.

The dissociation energies of gaseous diatomic oxides have now been established for most of the elements, largely through vaporization studies. Diatomic sulfide dissociation energies are not nearly so numerous, but investigations at several institutions are now under way. At present, data are available at least on the following pairs: MnO - MnS, TiO - TiS, LaO - LaS, and UO - US. The data now available reveal that the sulfide molecules are less stable than the oxides—a result that surprises no one—and that the ratio of dissociation energies is about 0.7. No satisfactory treatment of these dissociation energies, or even of their relationships to one another, is yet available. A major theoretical problem is the accurate computation of these energies from first principles, a problem on which some work is under way. When this problem has been solved, a most desirable subsequent direction of work would be the development of a qualitative description of the energetics of chemical binding in these simple molecules so that reasonably reliable predictions can be made.

The second area requiring investigation is that of the energies of solids. Consider the rare earth elements. The hugh difference in the volatility of the metals themselves is well known. Studies on the borides and carbides of these elements show that large differences exist between the energies of the corresponding phases for the different elements. Hence the mode of vaporization varies from one to another. These changes should be elucidated, and theoretical studies to understand them should be undertaken. The energy relationships among the several shear structures such as Ti_nO_{2n-1} ought to be a fruitful field of work.

Complicated gaseous molecules from inorganic systems constitute a third major area deserving future attention. Recent studies of the vaporization properties of the ternary titanium - vanadium - oxygen system have shown the existence of complex molecules arising from reactions between the sample and its tungsten crucible. Among these are $TiWO_4$, VWO_4, VW_2O_8, and many others. Mass spectrometric discoveries of many high-molecular-weight ions arising from sulfur-rich boron sulfide open a host of problems for future study. The high-molecular-weight ions that contain only boron and sulfur appear to originate with neutral polymers of BS_2. Ions are formed by simple ionization and fragmentation in the ion source and by metastable decomposition in the flight path. Other high-molecular-weight ions also appearing in the same experiments contained hydrogen, oxygen, or silicon. The relationships of these groups of ions one to another need to be clarified. Structures, appearance potentials, and thermodynamic properties are all to be measured and interpreted.

These particular examples from the Ti - V - O and boron sulfide studies serve to illustrate the great opportunities for both theoretical and experimental studies in the area of high-molecular-weight inorganic species. Surely many more systems will be shown to yield complex species. The future of this field cannot be foreseen at present, but an understanding of the structural and energy relationships among these substances, which are intermediate in complexity between most inorganic molecules and the larger ones of biological interest, should surely be of great use for understanding the chemistry of living systems.

A fourth area in high-temperature chemistry for which the future is especially bright is that of the kinetics and mechanism of high-temperature reactions. In this difficult field, the most obvious place to start is with well-characterized vaporization reactions. Detailed studies with the aid of mass spectrometers should ultimately lead to the clarification of the energies and natures of the various steps by which atoms pass from their equilibrium positions in a crystal to sites on the surface where they assume the configuration they must ultimately exhibit in the gaseous phase. Initial studies in this area should probably be designed to obtain reliable vaporization coefficients.

Thus, from the energetics of simple gaseous molecules, solid-state chemistry, and the structure and energetics of complex gaseous species, to the kinetic study of high-temperature reactions, many problems have been uncovered by recent work. Their solutions merit attention.

The author is pleased to acknowledge the support of the U.S. Atomic Energy Commission under contract No. AT(11-1)-1140.

Problems in
High-Temperature High-Pressure Research

J. R. SOULEN
Pennsalt Chemicals Corporation
King of Prussia, Pennsylvania

I should like to draw on some of our research experiences at Pennsalt to illustrate how current and future problems in high-temperature chemistry might be analyzed. These problems can be dealt with effectively only by studying individually each aspect of high-temperature chemistry that is important or by re-examining aspects that have appeared promising in the past but are thus far disappointing in results, and then trying to pinpoint the reasons for lack of progress. The particular area of our research used as an illustration is the synthesis of novel materials at very high pressures and temperatures, carried out largely by my colleague, M. S. Silverman. It has been stated (1) that some years ago high-pressure synthesis held great promise, but that not nearly so many new materials have been found as expected.

Let us first refer to Figure 1 and consider all the activities in which a person in high-temperature high-pressure research might find himself involved at any particular instant. Whatever one's object, certain materials are chosen and subjected to high-pressure and high-temperature conditions, as designated in Areas 1 and 2 of the figure. Some time must also be spent on operations indicated in Areas 2a, 2b, and 2c. Many workers, in fact, devote most of their efforts to these operations. In high-pressure research, new equipment and techniques continue to be developed. Improved pressure and temperature calibrations are of concern to a number of investigators. And, as also stated earlier, one can gather considerable data relating to structures and properties of materials under high-pressure conditions without being concerned that most of these will undergo rapid reversible changes, and no new materials are obtained after decompression. Those interested in new chemistry of a more permanent nature will follow through to operations in Areas 3 through 6 of Figure 1, and beyond this, work in Areas 7 and 8 will occupy those who wish to find uses for novel materials.

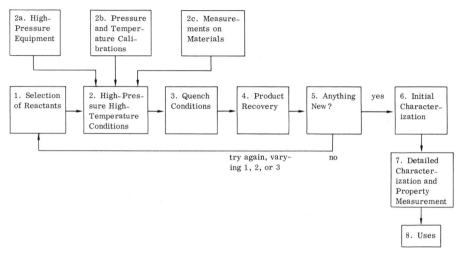

Figure 1. High-pressure synthesis.

Now let us limit our attention to the steps required to discover new materials using the very high-pressure and high-temperature conditions that have been relatively accessible now for almost a decade. To do this we must realize that the very type of work that has given us these new synthetic conditions must now be pushed into the background. Areas 2a and 2b deserve attention only during initial setting up of the laboratory, periodic checking, and when things go wrong; Area 2c can be almost completely ignored. And, desirable as they may be from other standpoints, all further characterization and measurements of a material following establishment of its novelty must detract from the effort to find still more new materials, unless the manning level is increased. Consequently, work in Areas 7 and 8 must also be held in tight check in programs where novel synthesis is the major object. This leaves Areas 1 through 6 as the essential ones in which chemists specializing in high-pressure synthetics must spend most of their time.

For our work, we purchased high-pressure equipment of very modest size, capable of reaching a pressure of 80 kb and a temperature of 2,500°C. It has served us admirably for over 5 years. Minimal time was spent in pressure and temperature calibrations, but these have been proved adequate by the achievement of identical synthetic results with much larger equipment elsewhere. In addition to selection of reactions for study, the major part of our time has been spent, not in the high-pressure aspects of the work, but rather in microscopic observation and characterization of high-pressure products and in careful qualitative and quantitative analysis of these products. We have had the good fortune to identify a number of novel materials that are stable indefinitely after decompression. Some of these are sufficiently well defined to be described in the literature (2), and the remainder are in earlier stages of characterization.

Admittedly, this is a difficult type of research, but I feel, nevertheless, that only its surface has been scratched. If its full potential is to be realized, this research must be supported in laboratories where there is the greatest chance of discovering new materials. This requires both primary interest in synthesis and characterization rather than in equipment and measurements and strong and intimate backing of the research man by extensive analytical and shop facilities. Money earmarked for research in high-pressure synthesis will be best spent in laboratories meeting these requirements.

Scores of other high-temperature research and measurement areas have been mentioned during this conference in which results are needed or work is desirable. Becoming aware of these, however, is only a small first step, and the process of agreeing upon degrees of importance and of arranging priorities in attacking problems is but a relatively small second step. The real key to accelerating progress is analysis similar to the above in each separate area in order to determine the kind of people, outlook, and facilities required. These will differ considerably from problem to problem, of course. Finally, there may be the even more difficult problem of finding the specific individual or group able to undertake a specific research assignment, or, if necessary, able to establish new facilities to carry it out.

This work was supported in part by the Office of Naval Research and by the U.S. Army Research Office, Durham, North Carolina.

REFERENCES

1. H. T. Hall, "High Temperatures, High Pressures and Periodic Compounds," this volume, page 65.
2. M. S. Silverman and J. R. Soulen, J. Phys. Chem., 67, 1919 (1963); M. S. Silverman, Inorg. Chem., 3, 1041 (1964); M. S. Silverman and J. R. Soulen, Inorg. Chem., 4, 129 (1965); M. S. Silverman, Inorg. Chem., 4, 587 (1965); M. S. Silverman, Inorg. Chem., in press.

Areas in Which
More High-Temperature Phase-Equilibrium Research is Needed

A. M. ALPER
Corning Glass Works
Corning, New York

In recent years there has been an increasing need to understand the behavior of materials at fluctuating high temperatures in a variety of atmospheres. Phase diagrams are useful tools for predicting what changes might take place under these conditions (1). Since little phase-equilibrium work has been done at temperatures above 2,000°C, many problems remain to be solved.

The following is a partial list summarizing the needs of various areas of high-temperature phase-equilibrium research:

1. Further research is needed concerning liquidus temperatures .above 2,000°C in binary systems and, in particular, in ternary and quaternary systems.

2. Studies are needed of phase stability of materials at these very high temperatures and of the effect of ions in solid solution on the phase-transformation temperatures.

3. Study is required of the effect of atmosphere on phase composition and phase stability at high temperatures, in particular with respect to how the stoichiometry of the phases changes as the temperature or atmosphere is changed. (Very little work similar to that of A. Muan and J. White, but at higher temperatures, has been done on stoichiometry of phases.)

4. More kinetic studies conducted in conjunction with phase-diagram studies are needed. For example, more work like that of Stubican and Roy (2), on the rate of unmixing of solid solutions with changing temperature, composition, or atmosphere, would be useful. More work on the rate of high-temperature phase transformations would also be valuable. T T T (time, temperature, transformation) diagrams are needed for ceramic systems.

5. More work should be done on phase equilibrium at high temperatures (> 1,500°C) and high pressures. Only a minor amount of work has been done in this area.

6. Unusual systems, such as oxides plus fluorides, should be studied. Initial data collected by our group at Corning Glass Works indicate that solid solution of fluoride ions in oxides is often observed at high temperatures. For example, fluoride ions are soluble in periclase (MgO) and in spinel at high temperatures. In the book, Phase Diagrams for Ceramists (3), no data are shown on the solid solubility of fluoride ions in oxides or on the solubility of oxide ions in fluorides. More research is also essential in other mixed-anion systems.

7. Very little work has been done showing the relation of temperature - composition phase diagrams to free-energy charts. A great deal of this work has been done in metallic systems; however, their relation is rarely shown in high-temperature ceramic systems.

8. Better methods of interrelating and describing multicomponent systems in a useful manner would be desirable. L. Brewer's work on methods for interrelating and predicting multicomponent systems, described in his article, "Prediction of High-Temperature Metallic Phase Diagrams" (4), is a big step in that direction. Perhaps Eskola's facies technique for handling multicomponent systems and phase assemblages, which is used in analyzing metamorphic rocks, can be modified and adapted for use in complex multicomponent systems.

9. Methods of using phase diagrams to solve particular problems should be discussed more often in articles on particular systems. Perhaps each scientist who works out a phase diagram should include a discussion of how this phase diagram might be used to increase understanding of high-temperature chemistry and technology.

10. When phase diagrams are determined, related information might be obtained that, if published, would be helpful to readers. For example, information about the time requirements and difficulties encountered in reaching equilibrium and information covering types of defects formed when solid solution occurs at high temperatures would be useful if included with the discussion of the phase diagrams.

11. The study of high-temperature molten phases and their stability regions has been neglected. A review of published phase diagrams indicates that there should be many more showing liquid immiscibility areas than those indicated in the present published diagrams.

12. Published diagrams of ceramic systems should be related to each other in order to determine general principles that will be helpful in predicting what phases might be stable at high temperatures and what compounds exist in complex systems. The work of Ramberg (5), Dietzel (6), Brewer (4), Vorres (7), and others is very useful, but more analyses like those should be done.

13. Improvement is needed in the techniques of determining phase diagrams. The following are some existing needs:

a. Better methods of characterizing samples;
b. Better methods of grinding and mixing samples without contamination;
c. Better methods of high-temperature measurement;
d. Better techniques for rapidly quenching solid samples;
e. Better methods for detecting phase changes at very high temperatures;
f. Better techniques for atmosphere control at these very high temperatures;
g. Better techniques to eliminate chemical contamination, in particular from crucibles;
h. Better techniques of studying systems that contain components having very high vapor pressures;
i. Better techniques of characterizing and analyzing phases after the experiments have been completed;
j. Better high-temperature x-ray equipment and better high-temperature optical and electron microscopes.

REFERENCES

1. A. M. Alper, Science of Ceramics, 3, to be published (presented at University of Bristol, July 1965).
2. V. S. Stubican and R. J. Roy, J. Phys. Chem. Solids, 26, 1293 (1965).
3. E. M. Levin, C. R. Robbins, and H. F. McMurdie, Phase Diagrams for Ceramists, The American Ceramic Society (1964).
4. L. Brewer, in High-Strength Materials, V. F. Zackay, ed., Wiley, New York (1965), pp. 12-103.
5. H. Ramberg, Am. Mineralogist, 39, 256 (1954); J. Geol., 61, 318 (1953).
6. A. Dietzel, Z. Elektrochem., 48, 9 (1942).
7. K. S. Vorres, J. Am. Ceramic Soc., 46, 410 (1963).

Research Needs Concerning
the Properties of Refractory Metal Oxides

R. N. McNALLY
Corning Glass Works
Corning, New York

Within the last 10 years, much work has been done on high-temperature materials. The arbitrary definition of high temperature referred to here is, any temperature for which the optical pyrometer is employed—in particular, temperatures in the range 2,000-3,000°C. For this temperature range, very little data concerning physical properties of materials have been reported in the literature. Some elementary data, such as melting points of these materials, have shown great variances among workers. A compilation of melting points of some common refractory materials, as determined in the Fused Refractories Research Department of Corning Glass Works, is shown in Table 1. S. J. Schnieder presented a compilation of the melting points of the metal oxides as gathered from the literature (1). Much scatter was noticed between the work done by different experimenters. This compilation points out the need for more work to be done on the measurement of melting points of these metal oxides, an area of research to which little attention has been paid by scientists in the last 50 years or more.

An acceptable standard for temperature calibration does not exist in the temperature range 2,000-3,000°C; therefore, a reproducible internal standard which yields an estimated calibration must be used in a laboratory. In the Corning Laboratory, under carefully controlled conditions, it was found that Al_2O_3 was reproducible, but from the viewpoint of accuracy this is an unsatisfactory method. It is obvious that some very careful melting-point determinations are needed on well-characterized single crystals of several refractory metal oxides. The most meaningful results will require as close to ideal experimental conditions as possible, especially with regard to temperature measurement, atmosphere control, contamination, sighting medium, and emissivity measurements.

TABLE 1. Melting Points of Common Refractory Materials

Metallic Oxide	Melting Point	Literature Value
MgO	$2,825 \pm 20\,^{\circ}C$ N_2 atmos. (4)	$2,852\,^{\circ}C$[a]
Al_2O_3	$2,043 \pm 10\,^{\circ}C$ (N_2, Ar air atmos.) (4)	$2,072\,^{\circ}C$[a]
Cr_2O_3	$2,330\,^{\circ}C$ (in air) $2,315\,^{\circ}C$ (in N_2) (4)	$1,849$–$2,424\,^{\circ}C$[b]
CaO	$2,625\,^{\circ}C$ (in N_2) (5)	$2,614\,^{\circ}C$[a]
ZrO_2	$2,700\,^{\circ}C$ (argon)	$2,519$–$2,850\,^{\circ}C$[b]
33% MgO – 67% CaO eutectic	$2,370\,^{\circ}C$ (in N_2) (5)	$2,300 \pm 50\,^{\circ}C$ (2)
35% MgO – 65% Cr_2O_3 eutectic	$2,355\,^{\circ}C$ (in N_2) (6)	$\sim 2,150\,^{\circ}C$ (3)
45% MgO – 55% Al_2O_3 eutectic	$1,995\,^{\circ}C$ (in N_2) (7)	$2,030\,^{\circ}C$ (2)
28.3% MgO – 71.7% Al_2O_3 (spinel)	$2,105\,^{\circ}C$ (in N_2) (7)	$2,135\,^{\circ}C$ (2)
21% MgO – 79% Cr_2O_3 (spinel)	$2,400\,^{\circ}C$ (in N_2) (6)	$\sim 2,200\,^{\circ}C$ (3)

[a] Preferred values from reference 1.

[b] Values from reference 1.

Perhaps a centrally located "bank" is needed where selected standards can be stored and available on loan. This would allow each high-temperature laboratory the use of the same accepted standard for calibration. Such a bank was suggested by Professor J. L. Margrave and other speakers at the International High-Temperature Symposium in Asilomar, California, in September 1963.

In addition, more work is needed on other fundamental properties that are of interest to researchers in the high-temperature field, such as surface tensions, densities, viscosities, and thermal and electrical conductivities.

Very few surface-tension measurements have been reported in the literature for the more-refractory metal oxides (2,000-3,000° C). Table 2 lists surface-tension values for Al_2O_3 taken from literature (8). Surface-tension measurements on other metal oxides such as MgO, CaO, ZrO_2, or Cr_2O_3 are nonexistent. Since surface tension is an important property in the flow of molten liquids and in thermodynamic calculations, such as surface entropy and surface energy, this is an important area of research to which little effort is currently directed.

TABLE 2. Surface-Tension Range of Al_2O_3[a]

	dynes/cm
W. D. Kingery	663–713
H. Von Wartenberg et al.	500–640

[a] From reference 8.

A careful examination of the drop-weight technique for high-temperature measurements (9) appears desirable.

REFERENCES

1. S. J. Schneider, Compilation of the Melting Points of the Metal Oxides, Natl. Bur. Std., Monograph 68, U.S. Govt. Printing Office, Washington, D.C. (1963).
2. G. A. Rankin and H. E. Merwin, J. Am. Chem. Soc., 38, 568 (1916).
3. W. T. Wilde and W. J. Rees, Trans. Brit. Ceramic Soc., 42, 126 (1943).
4. R. N. McNally, F. I. Peters, and P. H. Ribbe, J. Am. Ceramic Soc., 44, 491 (1961).
5. R. C. Doman, J. B. Barr, R. N. McNally, and A. M. Alper, J. Am. Ceramic Soc., 46, 313 (1963).
6. A. M. Alper, R. N. McNally, R. C. Doman, and F. G. Keihn, J. Am. Ceramic Soc., 47, 30 (1964).
7. A. M. Alper, R. N. McNally, R. H. Ribbe, and R. C. Doman, J. Am. Ceramic Soc., 45, 263 (1962).
8. W. D. Kingery, J. Am. Ceramic Soc., 42, 6 (1959).
9. A. W. Peterson, H. Kedesdy, P. H. Keck, and E. Schwarz, J. Appl. Phys., 29, 213 (1958).

QUESTION ADDRESSED TO DR. HORTON

QUESTION BY JOHN L. MARGRAVE: What will be the likely fate of the IUPAC bibliographies of high-temperature literature in view of the recent changes in the IUPAC subcommissions?

ANSWER: At the July 1965 Conference of IUPAC, the Commission on High Temperatures and Refractories which had consisted hitherto of two subcommissions, one for the gaseous state and one for the condensed state, was reduced in size. The Sub-Commission on Gases was dissolved, and attempts to reconstitute it within the Physical Chemistry Division have so far been to no avail. The IUPAC bibliographies have in the past consisted of three essentially simultaneous editions. One is a multilingual edition; essentially English, French, and German, i.e., references are in the language of the original article. This is published and distributed by our French colleagues on the commission. The English-language edition is published with the assistance of the U.S. National Bureau of Standards. In fact, J. J. Diamond of NBS contributes to and organizes the material, translates titles, and oversees the publication and distribution processes. These two editions reference only articles on the liquid and solid states. A third edition (in English) is reproduced and distributed by NBS and contains references to articles concerning gases. NBS does not assist in compiling this latter edition, in contrast to the condensed-state editions.

The role of IUPAC in the publication of these bibliographies has been to provide a means of contacting some contributors and of establishing a few editorial policies. This role has been played by the two subcommissions for the corresponding publications. If the Sub-Commission on Gases remains officially dissolved from the IUPAC it is very likely that NBS will discontinue its assistance in publishing the gas bibliography. With the continuing existence of a condensed-state subcommission, however, the corresponding edition of the bibliography is expected to continue with the assistance supplied by NBS, as heretofore.

Summary of Answers to Questionnaire

QUESTION: Are existing journals adequate for prompt publication of high-temperature data?

ANSWER: Both yes and no answers were recorded in about equal numbers. There was general recognition that the scatter of papers on high-temperature research creates a difficult problem for the researcher who tries to keep up with the current literature. Most of the data available seem to get published, but it would be helpful if there were at least a concentration of papers in two or three selected journals.

An exception was noted for detailed thermodynamic data, as they are often reported in calorimetric experiments or vapor-pressure measurements. Some journal should be devoted to complete tabulation of original data and pertinent experimental details. Members of the Calorimetry Conference have suggested a journal of thermochemistry and thermodynamics. There has also been a suggestion from several high-temperature chemists that a special journal for high-temperature data be founded. There already exist, of course, both French and Russian journals for high-temperature chemistry.

QUESTION: Is high-temperature research adequately financed by industry? Government agencies? other sources?

ANSWER: As expected, the answers were predominantly negative, and essentially all the respondents felt that more financial support for high-temperature research was desirable. In particular, a criticism of some of the sources was that, even if there were adequate financing, the financing was not always carefully organized and directed.

QUESTION: Are there enough high-temperature chemists?

ANSWER: Again, the respondents agreed that there were not enough good high-temperature scientists and recommended that universities do a more thorough job of acquainting students with new ideas and techniques that are available so that they can perform more efficiently when they go into actual high-temperature research.

QUESTION: In your opinion, what are the two most important high-temperature problem areas which need attention?

ANSWER: Several problem areas were mentioned often. These include (a) basic property measurements on a great variety of species, (b) surface phenomena and kinetics of gas-condensed phase reactions, (c) chemical syntheses utilizing high-temperature species, (d) high-temperature studies of solid-state phenomena, and (e) development of new concepts and diagnostic techniques for characterizing high-temperature systems.

QUESTION: Do high-temperature scientists meet often enough and keep up with new developments?

ANSWER: Most of the respondents felt that there were sufficient meetings for the specialists to meet and exchange information. A feeling was expressed that opportunities to discuss in detail the current advances, such as those afforded at the various Stanford Research Institute High Temperature Meetings, are especially valuable and should be continued.

It would appear that the organization of high-temperature scientists is so loose that there is considerable divergence in short-range as well as long-range goals. Some planning efforts would seem desirable to see that important areas are being considered and to evaluate progress at regular intervals.

QUESTION: Is there an instrument or technique which could contribute uniquely to the development of our understanding of high-temperature phenomena?

ANSWER: There is general recognition of the need for more sophisticated mass spectrometers, electron microprobes, velocity selectors, and shock tubes. There were suggestions that high-temperature scientists might conceivably be making more use of large-scale high-temperature facilities such as rockets, re-entry vehicles, and ballistic ranges. High-temperature experiments need not necessarily be performed with small apparatus in an earthbound laboratory.

Participants

A. M. Alper, Corning Glass Works, Corning, N.Y.

R. Badachhape, Department of Chemistry, Rice University, Houston, Texas

R. F. Baddour, Department of Chemical Engineering, Massachusetts Institute of Technology, Cambridge, Massachusetts

Charles W. Beckett, National Bureau of Standards, Washington, D.C.

Gottfried Besenbruch, Department of Chemistry, Rice University, Houston, Texas

Melvin G. Bowman, Los Alamos Scientific Laboratory, Los Alamos, New Mexico

Leo Brewer, Inorganic Materials Research Laboratory, University of California, Berkeley, California

C. H. Chang, Department of Chemistry, Rice University, Houston, Texas

T. V. Charlu, Department of Chemistry, Rice University, Houston, Texas

William A. Chupka, Argonne National Laboratory, Argonne, Illinois

Daniel Cubicciotti, Stanford Research Institute, Menlo Park, California

Robert P. Epple, Division of Research, U.S. Atomic Energy Commission Washington, D.C.

J. B. Ezell, Department of Chemistry, Rice University, Houston, Texas

Peter Ficalora, Department of Chemistry, Rice University, Houston, Texas

Robert H. Fox, Research and Engineering Support Division, Institute for Defense Analysis, Arlington, Virginia

J. L. Franklin, Jr., Department of Chemistry, Rice University, Houston, Texas

Paul W. Gilles, Department of Chemistry, University of Kansas, Lawrence, Kansas

A. V. Grosse, Temple Research Institute, Temple University, Philadelphia, Pennsylvania

Earl A. Gulbransen, Division of Physical Chemistry, Westinghouse Electric Corporation, Pittsburgh, Pennsylvania

H. Tracy Hall, Department of Chemistry, Brigham Young University, Provo, Utah

Robert Hauge, Department of Chemistry, Rice University, Houston, Texas

Amos G. Horney, Air Force Office of Scientific Research, Arlington, Virginia

William S. Horton, National Bureau of Standards, Washington, D.C.

S. J. Hruska, Metallurgical Engineering Department, Purdue University, Lafayette, Indiana

Myron Kaufman, Department of Chemistry, Harvard University, Cambridge, Massachusetts

Vishwa M. Khanna, Department of Chemistry, Rice University, Houston, Texas

Robert L. Lad, Lewis Research Center, National Aeronautics and Space Administration, Cleveland, Ohio

W. J. Leahy, Air Force Rocket Propulsion Laboratory, Edwards, California

Rex B. McLellan, Department of Mechanical Engineering, Rice University, Houston, Texas

R. N. McNally, Corning Glass Works, Corning, N.Y.

John L. Margrave, Department of Chemistry, Rice University, Houston, Texas

Joseph F. Masi, Air Force Office of Scientific Research, Arlington, Virginia

L. S. Nelson, Aerospace Science Division, Sandia Corporation, Albuquerque, New Mexico

Martin A. Paul, National Academy of Sciences - National Research Council, Washington, D.C.

S. S. Penner, Department of Aerospace and Mechanical Engineering Sciences, University of California, San Diego, California

Kenneth S. Pitzer, President, Rice University, Houston, Texas

George B. Rathmann, Minnesota Mining and Manufacturing Company, St. Paul, Minnesota

Zevi W. Salsburg, Department of Chemistry, Rice University, Houston, Texas

Harold L. Schick, Aerospace Division, Lockheed Missiles and Space Company, Palo Alto, California

Alan W. Searcy, Department of Mineral Technology, University of California, Berkeley, California

John I. Slaughter, Martin Company, Division of Martin Marietta Corporation, Baltimore, Maryland

J. R. Soulen, Contract Research Department, Pennsalt Company, King of Prussia, Pennsylvania

David R. Squire, U.S. Army Research Office, Durham, North Carolina

S. Strauss, Research Technical Division, Bowling Air Force Base, Washington, D.C.

William Weltner, Jr., Research Institute, Union Carbide, Tarrytown, New York

C. Herndon Williams, Sandia Corporation, Albuquerque, New Mexico

James Wood, Department of Chemistry, Rice University, Houston, Texas

Kiro Zmbov, Department of Chemistry, Rice University, Houston, Texas